10

REE

GAS STREET

JAN NEEDLE

Resource Material and Extension Work
Stephen Cockett

Additional Material
Vivien Gardner

Series Consultant
Cecily O'Neill

COLLINS EDUCATIONAL

Copyright © 1986 Jan Needle and Stephen Cockett

First published 1986, reprinted 1987, 1989

ISBN 0 00 330232 6

Author's note

'The Rebels of Gas Street' is not my favourite title for this play, and if you can think of a better one, feel free to use it. It was originally called 'The Battle of Royton Sands', and I think 'Gas Street and Mumps' is also pretty good. Perhaps you could find a title which is appropriate to the area you live in.'

JN

Acknowledgements

Cover photograph, The British Library; BBC Hulton Picture Library, pages vi, 55, 63, 64 (top and btm), 78 (top and btm), 83; The Mansell Collection, pages vii, 58, 73; Greater London Council Photograph Library, pages 67, 68.

Artwork by Kate Shannon

Design by The Pinpoint Design Company

Typeset by Hope Services, Abingdon. Reproduced, printed and bound by Bell and Bain, Glasgow.

CONTENTS

INTRODUCTION

During the summer of 1911, as temperatures soared, more and more workers answered the call to strike, until it seemed that only the school children were still working. The first of the school strikes broke out on 5th September at Bigyn Street School, Llanelly. An assistant teacher was taking the top class in place of the headmaster who was away sick. A note was passed round the class suggesting a strike. The teacher

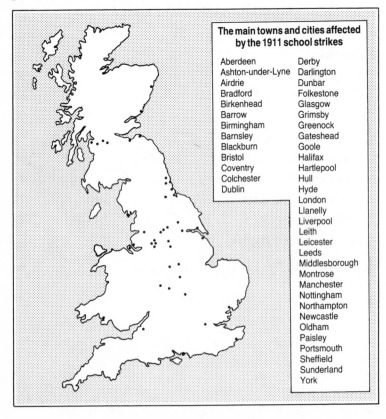

The main towns and cities affected by the 1911 school strikes

Aberdeen	Derby
Ashton-under-Lyne	Darlington
Airdrie	Dunbar
Bradford	Folkestone
Birkenhead	Glasgow
Barrow	Grimsby
Birmingham	Greenock
Barnsley	Gateshead
Blackburn	Goole
Bristol	Halifax
Coventry	Hartlepool
Colchester	Hull
Dublin	Hyde
	London
	Llanelly
	Liverpool
	Leith
	Leicester
	Leeds
	Middlesborough
	Montrose
	Manchester
	Nottingham
	Northampton
	Newcastle
	Oldham
	Paisley
	Portsmouth
	Sheffield
	Sunderland
	York

intercepted the note and caned the boy responsible, whereupon the class protested and stormed out, sending a picket to Lakefield School.

Upon hearing the news, the headmaster got up from his sick bed to confront the strikers and persuaded them to return to school. However, the next day, pupils of Lakefield School, Llanelly protested against the change in hours of morning lessons and held a demonstration in the playground, and pupils of Edgehill School, Liverpool left their desks and picketed the school gates.

During the next week, strike fever spread to schools in over 60 towns and cities.

The play you are about to read draws together characters, issues and events to help you recreate this long forgotten story and bring it alive in action.

Following the play, you will find a selection of pictures and newspaper reports about the strikes, as well as background information and stories about school and home life in 1911. Each section of the material contains ideas for further practical work and some suggestions for incorporating this work into the text.

The play and the resource material have a wide range of uses. Here are some of the possibilities:

Stage 1 ● Read the text.
● Use the resource material as starting points for discussion, writing in class and for independent drama sessions. This work could be linked with an historical study of social conditions in 1911.

Stage 2 ● Work towards a classroom performance of the play.
● Build in ideas and scenes arising from your study and work on the resource material. Suggestions for performing the play can be found on page 50.

Stage 3 ● Use your classroom performance as the basis for a more ambitious production involving an extended cast and drawing on resources from the music and art departments.

The play has an adaptable framework. Don't be afraid to alter it. The more you make the play your own, the more satisfying it will be. Bear in mind that the school strikes took place in many parts of the country and there could be a lot of fascinating material on your own doorstep. So carefully consider the possibilities of resetting the play in your own area using local characters and incidents. You will find advice on how to set about doing local research on page 53.

Rather than follow one particular strike story, the play draws on incidents and characters from strikes that happened nationwide. These are set against the backdrop of a town which itself saw some notable action by its young rebels — Oldham in Lancashire. Royton Sands, a key location in the drama, was an urban sand pit forty miles from the sea. On sizzling summer days the youth of Oldham would go there to find fresh air and fun as good as any to be had on the golden sands of Blackpool.

You may be a little surprised when you read the play to meet the characters of Queen Victoria and Sir Robert Peel (the man who set up the 'Peelers' in 1829) as they were both dead long before 1911. Their purpose in the play is to act as representatives of attitudes and values in society and government that had been inherited from a previous age and which found expression during the strikes. They are intended to be larger than life characters so it will be appropriate to use an exaggerated style when reading and performing them.

Queen Victoria

A Member of the Metropolitan Police Force

In a performance of the play, the authority figures, the upper and lower classes should occupy their own 'home-base' — with Queen Victoria preferably high up and the poor families low down. Even when reading through the play for the first time, it might be a good idea to group the characters and to place them in the room in a way which indicates their position on the social ladder.

From time to time as you read the play you will come across one of these:

Each signpost directs you to a section of the resource material which relates to the scene you are reading. There you will find ideas for background work and suggestions for adapting the play at the point where you meet the signpost.

THE CHARACTERS

Narrator
Queen Victoria
Sir Robert Peel
Lord Baden-Powell
Mr Whippem – headmaster of Gas Street Ragged School
Constable
Vicar

UPPER CLASSES
Mr Fanshawe – a magistrate
Mrs Fanshawe
Cynthia Fanshawe – their daughter
Cyril Fanshawe – their son
Lily and the girls of the Mumps Academy
The Boy Scouts

LOWER CLASSES
Mrs Atkins
Tommy Atkins – her son
Mrs Simkins
Sammy Simkins – her son
Daughters
Newsboy
Undertaker
Undertaker's assistant
Shopkeeper
The Mums of Oldham Town
Scruff Kids of Gas Street Ragged School, including:
    Polly Andrews – monitor
    Mary Ann Higginbottom
    Charlie Williams

THE REBELS OF GAS STREET

SCENE ONE

A street. Four distinct sets of people keeping themselves
obviously separate from one another. The **Scruff Kids** *play a*
boisterous street game, while the **Posh Children** *play a gentler*
one. The adult **Lower Orders** *gossip while donkey-stoning*
their doorsteps or working at the dolly-tub, say, while the
Upper Classes *pass snootily by.*
    The **Scruff Kids** *start singing, and everybody appropriate*
joins in. As they sing the last verse, the **Scruff Kids** *begin to*
approach the **Upper Classes** *and their children and beg in a*
threatening way, driving the **Upper Classes** *back into their*
'home base'.

TURN TO p.56

> Down at our school,
> It really is so funny,
> Kids do all the ruddy work
> But the teachers get the money.
>
> Down at our school,
> Amo amas amanting,
> Parrot this and parrot that —
> We're parrot-sick of chanting.
>
> Down at our school,
> The canes and straps are flying.
> They can't beat us down it's true —
> But it ain't for want of trying.
>
> Down at our school,
> it really is so funny.
> But if you want to see us,
> You'll have to pay some money:

1

Soldiers half a crown,
Sailors half a guinea,
Big fat men, two and ten —
Little kids a penny!

When the song is over, the **Narrator** *takes up his position. He is pompous and overdressed, with the delivery of a music hall presenter.*

NARRATOR   Ladies, gentlemen — and scruffs. As the strains of that appalling and subversive air die away, the time has arrived for me to do my duty as narrator. What you are about to witness is the portrayal of a slice of the illustrious history of our dear borough, Oldham.

Scruff Kids boo, **Upper Classes** *clap mildly.*

The portrayal, I say, of some important history, along with the re-enactment of a great battle, which was fought with unparalleled savagery, and enormous loss of life in the nearby watering place of Royton-by-the-Sea.

Scruff Kids cheer, **Upper Classes** *disapprove.*

During the course of this enactment, you will have the opportunity to meet, to observe, and to hear talking, some of the most important personages of that, this, or any other age. You will watch in awe the clear-thinking and splendid leadership of Sir Robert Peel, chief of the Oldham Constabulary.

Sir Robert, dressed as a comic policeman in stove-pipe hat, steps forward and bows — to boos, cheers and a brief fanfare.

You will gasp at the antics of Lord Baden-Powell, founder of the Scout Movement and more often remembered as the man who relieved Lady Smith than as one of Werneth's most famous sons.

Baden-Powell steps forward. He is in evening dress, but wearing shorts.

And last, but by no means least, you will listen intently to the pearls of wisdom as they drop from the very lips of her majesty Queen Victoria herself — the dear lady remembered so fondly as the inaugurator of sea-bathing at Royton.

Victoria, either a padded person in black, with the characteristic hair and posture of the later years of her reign, or a cardboard cut-out, is wheeled across the area by a bewigged flunkie in a pram or trolley from which she gives the 'royal wave'. The

*Upper Classes cheer and wave Union flags. The **Lower Orders** hiss, although they do not boo, and a few half-heartedly wave flags. The **Narrator** continues as she disappears.*

The better-educated among you may goggle at some of these things. Indeed, you may resent the gross and unfair way in which Baden-Powell's organisation is lampooned, and scouts in general presented as knock-kneed youths in overlong shorts or overshort longs, depending on point of view. Some may bitterly carp that the good late Queen had been dead for some ten years when these events took place, although her memory certainly lived on. Some may say that Sir Robert Peel was at no time a member, let alone head, of Oldham Constabulary. Some of you may even notice, though I doubt it, that Royton is not a seaside town at all. To all of this I can only reply: peel back your ears and listen; pin on your eyes and watch.

*The **Narrator** walks to the centre. The cast regroup.*

This much **is** true. In 1911 the summer was very hot, and very long. By the middle of it workers all over Britain had come out on prolonged and often viciously-repressed strikes. They started in Southampton, and spread to Liverpool, Hull, Manchester, Wales, Ireland. The docks were affected, as were the seamen, the railways, the canals, and the busmen. Mills were out, factories were closed, there was talk of a general strike. By the late summer it must have seemed that almost the only people left working were the schoolchildren. So, in September they decided to do something about it.

That is the scene. Here are the protagonists. Ladies and gentlemen — our hero. Whenever Mr Whippem, the headmaster, appears, you will of course cheer.

***Whippem** steps forward, swishing a long cane. **Upper Classes** applaud, **Scruff Kids** boo frantically.*

Here, at the head of the young people of the Mumps Academy for the Sons and Daughters of Gentlefolk, is our heroine, Miss Cynthia Fanshawe. Whenever she appears it is customary to go 'aah'.

***Cynthia** and the **Posh Children** step forward, looking sweet. 'Aahs' of approval overwhelmed by the **Scruff Kids'** 'yeerghs' of disgust.*

And finally, a hiss of horror and repugnance for the villain of the piece. The terror of Gas Street Ragged School, troublemaker and strikeleader: Tommy Atkins!

*Tommy leads the **Scruff Kids** forward. Tutting and a few ragged cheers.*

Thank you. And now, we proudly present: **The Rebels of Gas Street**!

SCENE TWO

The end of a hot Friday at Gas Street Ragged School. (The scene settings could be written out and paraded on a placard.)

*The **Scruff Kids** are seated in front of a blackboard, on which is written amo, amas, amat, etc. The **Monitor**, **Polly Andrews**, is going through it by rote, using a pointer.*

*Outside the classroom stands **Sammy Simkins**, who has been excluded.*

P. 71 TURN TO

POLLY ANDREWS   Amo.

PUPILS   Amo.

POLLY ANDREWS   Amas.

PUPILS   Amas.

POLLY ANDREWS   Amat.

PUPILS   Amat.

POLLY ANDREWS   Amamus.

PUPILS   Amamus.

POLLY ANDREWS   Amatis.

PUPILS   Amatis.

POLLY ANDREWS   Amant.

PUPILS   Amant.

POLLY ANDREWS   Again!

*They repeat it faster. At the end, **Polly Andrews** mops her brow.*

POLLY ANDREWS   I think you've got it. Now — Tommy Atkins. Can you tell me what it means?

TOMMY   *stands*   It's Latin, ain't it?

CHARLIE WILLIAMS   Nah, it's French, that. You're daft, Tommy Atkins.

MARY ANN HIGGINBOTTOM   I think it's Double-Dutch. And I should know.

4

Shouts of 'Rubbish!' 'Shut up!' 'Put a sock in it', etc.

POLLY ANDREWS   Silence! Silence! You wouldn't dare to do this if Mr Whippem wasn't away sick.

CHARLIE   That's as maybe. But he is, isn't he?

TOMMY   Why do you do it, anyway, Polly? You don't get paid for being a monitor. Is it the glory?

GIRLS   *led by* **Mary Ann**   Polly Andrews runs the class,
                                                    She likes sitting on her . . .

POLLY ANDREWS   Silence! Now, we'll do history. We are going to learn about the British Empire. On which the sun never sets. Those with slates, get them prepared.

As the kids scrabble about, **Tommy** *turns to* **Charlie***.*

TOMMY   It seems to me the sun never sets on this classroom, Charlie. I've never been so hot.

CHARLIE   It's a good job they've stuck Sammy Simkins in the corridor. Gor! The pong!

MARY ANN   He's been emptying the lavvies every night. His Dad's sick.

CHARLIE   Yeah, sick of the stink, Mary Ann. I wish we went to the posh school. They've had their lessons outside for the last five weeks.

POLLY ANDREWS   *lecturing*   It is a well-known saying, and a true one, that our Queen rules over an Empire upon which the sun never sets. In every part of the earth we have **colonies**, e.g. Australia and British North America, **subject states**, e.g. India, and **protectorates**, e.g. Cyprus and Egypt. As their names suggest, we have become possessed of these various . . .

As **Polly Andrews** *drones on, many of the children fall asleep.*

TOMMY   *to* **Charlie** *and* **Mary Ann**   Have you heard about them kids in Wales? They've gone on strike. I reckon we ought to call a meeting, after school.

MARY ANN   That's the best idea you've had all day, Tommy Atkins.

CHARLIE   Nah! Let's scrag old Smelly Simkins. The mucky little bleeder!

Freeze.

TURN TO p.77

5

SCENE THREE

*The scragging of 'Smelly' Simkins. After a few seconds of freeze, the **Scruff Kids** break away and surround **Sammy**, chanting.*

GIRLS   You smell!

BOYS   You stink!

GIRLS   You smell!

BOYS   You stink!

GIRLS   You smell!

BOYS   You stink!

GIRLS   You smell!

BOYS   You stink!

SAMMY   *in the middle of the circle, desperate*   I can't help it! I've got to do my father's job! He ain't well!

*The **Kids** turn to face outwards and all sing in unison.*

SCRUFF KIDS   The corporation muckcart was full right to the brim
When Smelly Simkins fell in it and found he could not swim.
He sank right to the bottom, just like a little stone.
And then we heard him singing:
There's no place like home . . .
There's no place like home.

*They run off, laughing. **Sammy** is left alone.*

SCENE FOUR

*The Fanshawes' home. The Fanshawes have just finished tea, and **Mr Fanshawe** is reading a newspaper. **Newsboy** appears with a placard and shouts the headlines while the family remain in tableau (i.e. they freeze in position).*

NEWSBOY   Chronicle, Chronicle, read all about it! Strikes in steel, cotton, coal, shipping, docks and transport. Five police horses destroyed after Liverpool riots. Troops kill two strikers in Wales. Read all about it!

MRS FANSHAWE *coming out of tableau as* **Newsboy** *leaves* Oh no! Not deaths! That is too, too terrible.

MR FANSHAWE Disgusting. Cynthia, to eat three slices of cake at one sitting is quite disgusting.

MRS FANSHAWE But can you do **nothing** about it, Charles? You are a magistrate, after all. **Deaths**!

CYNTHIA Only little bits, Daddy. I won't get fat, I promise you.

MRS FANSHAWE Charles, concentrate. Those **beasts** have killed five horses. Five poor, defenceless horses.

MR FANSHAWE Terrible. Appalling. But what can one do, my dear? One cannot deport them to the Colonies any more. One does one's best, I promise you.

MRS FANSHAWE It seems to me, Charles, that the entire fabric of our dear country is being undermined. I think Mr Churchill is quite right. They should all be shot.

CYNTHIA That's not fair, Mummy. Girls can't join the Army.

MR FANSHAWE In any case, my love, we could hardly shoot them all. At the last count there were nearly four hundred thousand men on strike. I doubt if the Army has that many bullets!

MRS FANSHAWE This is not a matter for jesting, dearest. A firm stand should be made.

CYNTHIA They could shoot just one from every factory, Daddy. Or five, perhaps.

MR FANSHAWE Darlings, we know best, I assure you. Firm action is being taken, never fear. Why, only this morning I sent one rogue to prison for three months for coming out on strike.

MRS FANSHAWE What was the charge?

MR FANSHAWE Neglecting his wife and children. Who were at the court, actually — and one **hundred** per cent behind him, although they are nearly starving! That will show the scum we mean business!

MRS FANSHAWE One man, for three months. It is hardly enough, Charles.

MR FANSHAWE There have been others, dear. Seventeen have been committed this week, by my hand alone. We will break their spirits, never fear.

MRS FANSHAWE   And now the very schoolchildren are talking of going on strike. Those awful ragged urchins down in South Wales.

MR FANSHAWE   That will not spread to this town, dear. Our authorities will treat them firmly. We will beat any such socialistic notions out of them.

CYNTHIA   Anyway, Father, the boys in this place would never strike. They don't have the gumption. They are milksops, one and all.

Cyril Fanshawe rushes on, dressed in Eton-type uniform. He throws himself, crying, at his father's feet.

CYRIL   Oh Father, Father, **do** something. The nasty boys have beaten me. They threw stones.

MRS FANSHAWE   *comforting him*   There there, Cyril, there there. Charles, this is intolerable. I insist that you take these children to a place of safety.

MR FANSHAWE   A place of safety!? What **can** you mean, woman?

MRS FANSHAWE   *to Cyril*   There there, diddums, don't you cry. Daddy will take us to the seaside for the weekend, won't you Daddy? We'll go to that nice private hotel at Blackpool.

CYNTHIA   Oh golly, Daddy, that **would** be nice . . .

*They go into tableau as **Newsboy** returns.*

P.66 TURN TO

NEWSBOY   Chronicle, Chronicle — read all about it! Another school in Llanelly joins strike epidemic. Flying pickets roam the town. Mr Churchill despatches troops to deal with miners. Read all about it!

SCENE FIVE

*The Atkins' home. **Tommy** and **Mrs Atkins** are doing the accounts.*

MRS ATKINS   It's no good, Tommy. We won't be able to pay the rent again next week. That'll be three weeks in a row. It will be the bailiff soon.

TOMMY   I reckon five and ninepence is too much, Mum. it's only a little dump.

8

MOTHER Yes dear, but the rats are friendly — and we do . . .

TOMMY and **MRS ATKINS** *this is a familiar routine* get free mushrooms off the damp patches on the wall.

TOMMY Yes, very funny. But it **is** too much. The landlord's a shark.

MRS ATKINS You're talking rubbish, Tom. If Mr Johnson wasn't such a kindly man, he'd have had us out weeks ago.

TOMMY Maybe. But what will he say now? How much do we owe him?

MRS ATKINS Three weeks at five and nine. You tell me. You're the scholar.

TOMMY *mumbles, working hard, and gives up* I dunno, Mum. They only seem to teach us foreign languages.

MRS ATKINS Oh Tommy!

TOMMY I could say 'I love you' in Latin if that would be a help.

MRS ATKINS So that's seventeen and threepence rent we owe, eleven shillings exactly to Mrs T. at the shop, and three shillings arrears for the burial insurance. And I've got nineteen and elevenpence in my purse. Oh Tommy.

TOMMY It's thirty-one days until Dad's going to be let out of prison. Do you think he'll go back to work then? Or will he stay on strike?

MRS ATKINS *sighs* If the strike's still strong, he'll stay out, won't he? It's the principle of the thing, Tom. Some things have got to be suffered for. He went on strike because they cut his wages from twenty-five shillings a week to twenty-three. And we can't live on twenty-three shillings and still eat, can we? So he'll stay on strike.

TOMMY But we can't live on nowt, neither. We're in debt and it's getting worse. How can striking help?

MRS ATKINS Because when the strike's won, we'll have **more** than twenty-five shillings a week. Then we'll pay off the debt. Simple. If the cause is just, a strike is justified. It's principle.

Pause.

TOMMY Mum?

MRS ATKINS Yes?

TOMMY   There's talk of the schools coming out, an' all. On strike. What do you reckon to that?

MRS ATKINS   *sharply*   Don't talk daft, Tommy! What grievances have you lot possibly got?

TOMMY   They don't teach us nothing useful, they stop us from doing jobs to make ends meet, they pull our hair and beat us with sticks, they tell us that strikers are traitors and the Government's always right. They teach us the bloody Latin for 'I love you'.

MRS ATKINS   *laughs*   And they give you an attendance medal and a nice report if you're good and don't play truant. You need that, Tommy. **We** need that. If your father never works again, your wage will be our lifeline.

TOMMY   Never works again! What do you mean?

MRS ATKINS   ·They shot two men in Wales today, son. Killed them. If the strikers don't win, anything could happen. Perhaps we'd better pay off the burial insurance arrears first!

TOMMY   Mum! We don't need stuff like that. We'll pull through. Look on the bright side.

MRS ATKINS   I do look on the bright side, Tommy, and there's a lot worse off than us, but we still pay off the burial insurance first. That's my decision.

TOMMY   All right, Mrs Morbid. But who are these worse off than us, then? I haven't tasted hot food for six days! And **you** brought up the subject of the bailiff just now!

MRS ATKINS   Well — Sammy Simkins in your class, for a start.

TOMMY   Smelly Simkins! He deserves to be! He pongs. His Dad shovels shit all night.

MRS ATKINS   His father died this afternoon, Tommy. And I doubt if **they** had burial insurance. They're **so** poor, Tommy, the bailiff doesn't bother calling any more.

*The **Scruff Kids** give a quick and very sprightly burst of song as the scene changes.*

KIDS   Down in our Coalhole,
Where muck slaps up winders,
We've used all our coal up, we're right down to cinders.
If the bum-bailiff calls,
He won't know where to find us.

P.61 TURN TO

'Cause we're
Right down in Coalhole,
Where muck slaps up winders!

SCENE SIX

*The Simkins' home. In the front room, Sammy's father is lying
'in state' under a thin blanket. Bone white face. Around him sit
Sammy's **sisters**, heads and faces hidden in shawls, mourning.
Sammy and **Mrs Simkins** are discussing funeral
arrangements with the **Undertaker**, a large, unpleasant man
with a black coat and top hat decorated with black crepe. His
Assistant giggles at what he considers to be his master's
witticisms.*

UNDERTAKER   A **coffin** is it? My my, you'll have to show
me a little more money before that could be considered.
Coffins come expensive.

SAMMY   But he can't be buried in a blanket, sir.

UNDERTAKER   Judging by the smell in here, sonny, he'd
better be buried rather sharpish, in whatever the receptacle!
I think he's gone off.

Assistant giggles.

MRS SIMKINS   Sir, must it be a pauper's grave? We kept up
the insurance payments until the very last minute. Until
everything else was gone.

UNDERTAKER   *checking paper*   According to my
information, that means the last minute occurred seven
weeks ago. **Very** unusual!

Assistant giggles.

MRS SIMKINS   But that's only seven shillings. And we'd
been paying for years. What about all that money?

UNDERTAKER   As the dead cannot take it with them,
Madam, so the living must live within their means. You
surely don't expect us to give you the money back, do you? It
was insurance. We have our overheads. We are a very
large . . . er, undertaking.

Assistant giggles.

SAMMY   If we paid the seven shillings now? What then?

UNDERTAKER Well, I'm not an unreasonable man, sonny. For an extra seven shillings you would get — an extra seven shillings' worth.

Assistant giggles.

SAMMY But still a pauper's funeral?

UNDERTAKER In a pauper's grave. Your insurance, madam and sir, has lapsed. By the way — do the windows in here open? There's an **awful** pong.

Sammy and Mrs Simkins confer.

MRS SIMKINS We haven't got no more, sir, I'm afraid.

UNDERTAKER I'm very sorry to hear it. You have my deepest sympathy. Right, we must away, we are busy men. We'll be round on Monday morning, then. Have you got a plank, at least?

SAMMY A plank? What for?

UNDERTAKER Very difficult to carry a stiff without a plank. Unless he's still stiff, of course!

Assistant giggles.

SAMMY Us carry him? Me and my Mum?!

UNDERTAKER *indicating the girls* Plenty of willing hands, ain't there? Don't expect the corporation to provide men, do you? Not for a pauper's do? Think yourselves lucky you're getting an 'ole in the ground! And two minutes of the duty parson's time.

MRS SIMKINS Two minutes!

UNDERTAKER Madam, farewell. Time is money, as the poet said. *Starts to leave* Although you **could** raise the extra by busking, maybe? That man of yours can certainly hum! Just my little joke!

Assistant giggles.

UNDERTAKER Until Monday, then. And please accept our deepest condolences in your hour of grief. For one and sixpence extra I'll repeat that in front of witnesses at the grave.

*They go. **Sammy** and **Mrs Simkins** join mourners round corpse. They sing, very sweetly and sadly as if it were a real funeral dirge.*

FAMILY There is a happy land, far, far away,
Where they have bread and jam, three times a day.
Oh how the angels yell,
When they hear the dinner bell.
There is a happy land, far, far away.

SCENE SEVEN

A high-class street. **Cynthia** *and her friend* **Lily** *wait to be taken to Blackpool.*

CYNTHIA Yes, Daddy's awfully mean. He **has** agreed to take us to Blackpool — reluctantly. And you as well, Lily. But he would **not** buy mother and me new dresses. He would not even **consider** it, in fact.

LILY My father's worse. He has **so** much money he honestly doesn't know what to do with it. But he won't let me have a sweet little dog to love.

CYNTHIA Of course, I understand Daddy's point. We're not made of money. And all these strikes as well. It's quite undermining the economy of the country, I understand. Things are really rather bad for the moneyed classes just at present.

LILY Mmm. My father had to close another factory last week, rather than pay those bloodsuckers. Fourpence more a week they wanted, the very idea! That's another thousand of them have been taught a jolly good lesson, anyway! He was in such a good mood that I asked for the doggy then and there, but he just would not hear of it.

CYNTHIA And my papa leaves us waiting in a public street, and me in this **shamingly** scruffy dress! Dreadful.

LILY Sometimes, Cynthia, we really do get treated jolly badly.

CYNTHIA Three whole months, I've had it Lily. Really, I sometimes wonder if life is worth living. Three whole months.

They sing 'Daddy Wouldn't buy Me a Bow Wow' as a duet. Verses ad lib.

TURN TO p.79

CHORUS Daddy wouldn't buy me a bow-wow (bow-wow),
Daddy wouldn't buy me a bow-wow (bow-wow).

I've got a little cat, I am very fond of that —
But I'd rather have a bow-wow-wow.

Cynthia's parents enter, *plus* **Cyril** *and* **a friend**.

MR FANSHAWE　Come on, girls. We're off to Blackpool at
last. Bates has done the plugs and stripped the gearbox down
and changed the oil. He's got the motor running fine. I've just
sent him off to have a good scrub at the standpipe, then we
can leave.

CYNTHIA　And jolly well about time too. That chauffeur is
downright idle, if you ask me.

SCENE EIGHT

Gas Street Ragged School — Monday morning. **Tommy** *is
standing in front of a blackboard, on which he's written the
demands: 'Less cane!' 'Half an hour's play a day!' 'A half-
holiday each week!' 'Monitors to be paid a penny a week!' 'Less
cane!' He is holding a pointer.*

TOMMY　Come on, you fools. They're all fair demands. If
they won't grant 'em — let's walk out!

POLLY ANDREWS　Tommy Atkins, you'll get more cane,
not less!

CHARLIE WILLIAMS　*shouts*　What's up with you, Polly
Andrews? We've put you down for a penny wages, haven't
we?

GIRLS　*led by* **Mary Ann**　Polly Andrews is a creep,
　　　　　　　　　　　　　She would like two bob a week!

TOMMY　It's spreading like wildfire! They're out in
Liverpool now! They're out in Manchester! They got toy
pistols and frightened the good lads into joining! They're out
all over London, and in Glasgow. They're out in Hull and
Halifax!

POLLY ANDREWS　They're out of their minds, Tommy
Atkins. And so are you. Wait till Mr Whippem gets to hear of
this!

MARY ANN　He's taken to his bed. He's a lily-livered
coward, Polly Andrews! We've got him on the run!

CHARLIE WILLIAMS　It's him that's caused all this. He's

14

cruel and he doesn't teach us nothing. He just frightens us and beats us with his stick.

POLLY ANDREWS Yes — and the assistant teacher's just run off to his house to tell him what's going on!

MARY ANN He never has, you liar!

POLLY ANDREWS I shouldn't waste a lie on a girl like you, Mary Ann Higginbottom.

TOMMY Is that right, Polly? Is Whippem being told? Will he be too ill to come?

CHARLIE WILLIAMS Don't let her scare you, Tommy! She's part of it! It's her what gives us all that stupid Latin!

GIRLS *led by **Mary Ann*** Amo, amas, amat,
Polly is a rat!
Amo, amas amat,
Polly is a rat!

TOMMY It's true, Polly! All we want is less stupid lessons. I can't even add up three weeks' rent when we owe it to the landlord! I can't even spell 'committed to prison' when me Dad gets chucked in jail! We want proper learning.

CHARLIE And no religion jammed down our throat three times a day. And no being told the working man is bleeding Britain dry.

MARY ANN And no being told our Dads are German agents for striking for a living wage!

Tommy springs onto a desk/chair/table.

TOMMY *singing strongly* Fall in and follow me
Fall in and follow me
Never mind a fig about the teacher

ALL, *except **Polly Andrews,** surging forward and joining in.* He can't beat yer!

TOMMY Stand on me, boys, I know the way to go.

*With a roar, **Mr Whippem** rushes in, swishing his cane. He is dressed in a nightshirt, slippers and a mortarboard. The children scatter, leaving **Tommy** standing on high.*

WHIPPEM Can't beat you, eh, Atkins?! You foolish, foolish youth! Can't beat you, eh!

15

Tommy *jumps down and races off, pursued by **Whippem**. Roaring and thrashing off-stage as the pupils sit and face front.*

POLLY ANDREWS   Amo.

PUPILS   Amo.

POLLY ANDREWS   Amas.

PUPILS   Amas.

MARY ANN   *to audience*   Poor Tommy's got a red-hot . . . bottom!

SCENE NINE

Cynthia *alone in a street. She is sitting down, chin in hands, fed up. She is fiddling with her broken boot strap. The* ***Newsboy*** *comes on, ignoring her.*

NEWSBOY   Chronicle! Chron! Bradford boys demand no more cane and an extra half-holiday every week! Loyal pupils beaten with sticks and stones! Temperature in London hits ninety-three! Highest level recorded in September since 1808! Read all about it! Chronicle! Chron!

*He leaves. **Tommy** wanders on. He is singing 'Fall In and Follow Me' half under his breath. He sees **Cynthia** and stops.*

TOMMY   *going close*   Hello. What's up with you?

***Cynthia**, pretending he's not there, fiddles more frantically with her boot strap.*

TOMMY   Why ain't you at school? You're at the Mumps Academy, ain't you?

Cynthia *does not reply. She fiddles on.*

TOMMY   I've got it! You're on strike!   *Jumps back in mock terror*   You're one of these socialists, ain't you! Fomenting unrest! You're a German agent!

Cynthia *stands up and stamps her foot.*

CYNTHIA   Horrid boy! I am **not** an agent! I am **not** a socialist! I am **not** a striker! How dare you **suggest** such a thing!

TOMMY   Well — why ain't you at school, then? And what's wrong with being a striker, anyway? There's a lot of it about, that's for sure!

CYNTHIA   Yes, and I'm not at school because of it. Daddy's motor came under attack. We were ambushed by some strikers. They threw stones and smashed the windscreen. The car was badly damaged.

TOMMY   Crikey. Are you hurt? Where's the motor? Did you run away?

CYNTHIA   *loftily*   No, silly, of course I didn't. It would take more than a howling mob of socialist traitors to frighten me. Anyway — it was yesterday. We were coming back from Blackpool. All the strikers are in prison, now, and it jolly well serves them right! I **hate** strikers. They should **all** be in prison. They should be **shot**.

TOMMY   Hey, I . . .   *swallows his pride and anger. He is strangely smitten*   Well, I . . .   Look — if it was yesterday, why aren't you at school? How is that because of the strikers?

CYNTHIA   Everything's to do with the strikers. They're dragging this country under. They attacked Daddy's car — so I had to walk to school, see? And then my boot strap broke. So here I am. I should have thought that that was obvious.

TOMMY   Your boot strap. Oh. Maybe I could . . . well . . . you know. It's a decent pair of boots you've got there, I must say. Maybe I could have a look?

CYNTHIA   They're not decent, they're rubbish. I've only worn them three times, and they're fit only for the dustbin. They cost a lot of money, as well. British workmanship, you see? It's not what it was. The workers are too busy being selfish to care. There's no pride any more.   *She has put her foot on the bench.* **Tommy** *has been bending over it*   Is there anything you can do?

TOMMY   I think I can see the problem. Yes. I think maybe I can . . .

CYNTHIA   *slamming her boot to the ground in horror*   I say! You're not . . . ! You're not . . . ? **You're** not a striker, are you? A socialist!?

TOMMY   *pause*   Put your boot back and don't worry. Everything'll be champion. *Cynthia puts her boot back on to the bench*   There. *Pause as he works*   It seems a pity, though. To chuck them in the bin. They're hardly worn.

CYNTHIA   Yes, Mrs Tranter — she's the housekeeper — she rather hinted that this morning, I thought. She has a daughter about my age. My father appeared quite warm towards the idea.

TOMMY   And?

CYNTHIA   Oh, Mother would not hear of it, of course. She told Mrs Tranter she ought to be ashamed. It is better to starve to death than beg, she said. She tried to get Daddy to sack her, afterwards. For even hinting.

TOMMY   Oh. And what did you think?

CYNTHIA   Well, at first I found the idea rather revolting. I mean — I don't like the idea of boots that I've worn actually **touching** the rather unwashed skin of the lower sort. But I wouldn't have minded that much. Some people really are quite poor, you know. They bring it on themselves, of course. But some people actually don't have boots. So I suppose I wouldn't have minded **that** much if Mrs Tranter were to take them.

TOMMY   But mother knows best.

CYNTHIA   Oh yes.   *Tommy puts her foot onto the ground* Oh have you finished? Oh you **clever** boy!   *Testing* I can **walk!** Look — shall we **have** a walk? Just a little one? It's much too hot to go to school now, isn't it? The hottest day for one hundred and three years, I believe. Are you busy, Mister . . . ?

TOMMY   Atkins. Tommy Atkins. No, I don't believe I am, Miss . . . ?

CYNTHIA   Actually, my name's Fanshawe. But you may call me Cynthia. My father is a magistrate. We live up by the park.

She starts to walk, and takes **Tommy***'s hand.* **Tommy** *hangs back.*

TOMMY   A magistrate. Oh, I . . . Oh.

CYNTHIA   Yes, isn't that fun? He sent those nasty men who ambushed us to prison himself. What a novel way to end a trip to Blackpool, wasn't it? Oh come **on**, Tommy. Don't hang back. It's such a lovely day.

TOMMY   I . . .

The **Newsboy** *comes on.*

NEWSBOY   Chronicle! Chron! Read all about it! Fifty school

18

strikers in Hull bathe naked in the river! Temperature tops all-time high. Reservoir fears grow as drought goes on! Read all about it!

Tommy and Cynthia have reached another area. They sit down.

TOMMY   What's it like in Blackpool, then? Is it nice?

CYNTHIA   But haven't you **been** there? Not ever? I thought everyone had been to Blackpool.

TOMMY   It's not the end of the world, you know. I've been around. Plenty of other places. I've been to Leeds, I have. And to Manchester. Twice.

CYNTHIA   Manchester! Who hasn't? I go to Manchester shopping with my mother. Lots of times. Haven't you been with yours?

TOMMY   *pause*   I haven't got one. I'm an orphan.

CYNTHIA   *Are* you?! Oh how **awful**! Oh, you lucky thing! I don't like my father that much, I often wish he was dead. Oh, how terrible!

TOMMY   *changing subject*   Aye, but what's it like at Blackpool then? Do they have bands there? And sideshows?

CYNTHIA   Oh, they've got the lot. There's miles and miles of proms, with piers and such, and the tramways, naturally, and . . .

TOMMY   Proms? What's them then?

CYNTHIA   Proms. Well, they're proms, aren't they? You know. Proms.

TOMMY   Oh.

CYNTHIA   And the sea comes rolling in — great big waves. And when the water's out, there's all this sand. Tons and tons of it. And there are donkeys, and jugglers, and ice cream and pop, and sweets, and roundabouts, and puppets, and palmists, and Pierrots. It's lovely.   *Pause*   Where do you go for you holidays then being an orphan and so on?

TOMMY   Holidays! That's a laugh! What's that mean?

CYNTHIA   Oh come on. You know what holidays are. I don't believe you've **never** had a holiday.

TOMMY   Well I . . . Well, me and the lads go down to Royton Sands. When we fancy a lark.

CYNTHIA   Royton Sands? **Royton** Sands? What, that awful dump near Chadderton? There's no beach there, silly!

TURN TO p. 79

TOMMY   Never said there was though, did I? Who said beach eh, Cleverclogs? I said sands. Great big pits. Mountains of the stuff; acres of it. Great for digging in and rolling, and fighting.

CYNTHIA   *not nasty; joking*   And I suppose they have donkey rides, and trams, and brass bands? Barrel organs and monkeys and fellows selling parkin!

TOMMY   Aye well they do, so there! May not be so grand as Blackpool, but I bet it's more fun, at that. Who needs the sea, anyway? Nasty wet, cold stuff.

CYNTHIA   How would you know? I bet you've never even seen it!

TOMMY   A lot you know then. That's all.

CYNTHIA   *pulling back from spoiling everything*   Royton Sands. Do they really have all that sort of thing? Bands and parkin and stuff?

TOMMY   *daring*   You'll have to come with me one time, won't you? And find out.

CYNTHIA   Come with you? To Royton Sands? Do you mean that?

TOMMY   We could take some sandwiches and some corporation pop. I could take me buttons and we could swap the other kids. Maybe get some spice.

CYNTHIA   Corporation pop? What's corporation pop when it's out?

TOMMY   *amazed*   You don't know anything, do you? Don't they teach you nowt at that posh school?

CYNTHIA   Well they teach me . . .   *she breaks off. The funeral of Mr Simkins is coming into view, led by a* **Vicar** *in robes. He is carrying a Bible, and a large turnip-shaped watch*   Tommy! Whatever is going on?! What's that awful **smell**?

TOMMY   Oh crimes! It's a funeral. It's poor old . . . Oh crimes!

CYNTHIA   Golly, I've never seen anything like this before! You don't **know** them, do you!?

TOMMY   *shamefacedly, as the procession gets nearer*   No. No, I've never seen 'em before in my life.

The **Vicar** *is extremely impatient, as the shawl-bedecked* **daughters** *struggle along with their father's corpse. It is*

wrapped in a blanket, and is very flexible and wobbly. **Sammy**
and **Mrs Simkins** *try to help, but the corpse keeps bending and
drooping on the ground.*

VICAR *intoning* Dearly beloved, I really must
insist! *Consults watch* We are running twelve minutes
late on a three-minute burial! Dearly beloved, lift up the
sacred remains of our brother departed sharply
there! *Consults watch* Oh heavens above, this is out-rage-
ee-oh-ous!

*He skips back and forth, dragging and pushing the family and
corpse along.*

CYNTHIA Tommy, what are they **doing**? Why haven't they
put him in a coffin! Don't they **care**?

TOMMY I don't know, Cynthia. Maybe they're
too . . . Maybe they . . .

VICAR *intoning* This is intolerable. Beloved sisters and
brother I can only allow you one more min-ute! This is dreadful!

As the procession almost disappears off-stage, a gang of **Scruff
Kids** *poke their noses in at the point the funeral procession first
appeared from.*

SCRUFF KIDS *chanting* Smelly Sammy's Dad is dead
Sammy's Dad's departed.
Sammy's Dad is dead and
gorn —
It smells as if God's . . .

Sammy, *with a roar, chases them off. The* **Vicar** *is enraged.*

VICAR This is insufferable! The chief mourner, behaving
like a hooligan! I will **not** stand for it!

He storms off in the opposite direction from the cortege. **Sammy**
comes back. **Tommy**, **Cynthia** *and* **Sammy** *alone.*

SAMMY Can you give us a hand, Tom? You could read a bit
out, maybe. Or at least make summat up, like. To sound like
religion, you know. Could you? Please? Tommy?

CYNTHIA *looking at* **Tommy** *in horror* You said you
didn't know them! Oh Tommy! They're . . . they're . . .
they're . . .

TOMMY *furiously* **Poor!**

He stamps off, after **Sammy. Cynthia** *stands alone.*

CYNTHIA *to herself* I wouldn't go to Royton Sands with
you if you were the last lad in Oldham. Or anywhere else for
that matter. *Music up, softly* You're a rude, bad-
mannered pig and I hate you.

She sings, very sweetly

CYNTHIA Don't touch my silk dress,
My mother can tell;
My boots are guinea-gold and yours are black-
lead.
My bonnet is blue,
My heart it is true
Pause
And I dare not be seen
With such rubbish as you!

The music goes on, as **Cynthia** *stands forlorn*

CYNTHIA *softly* And another thing, Tommy Atkins.
You're low, you're scruffy, you don't comb your hair and I bet
you talk with your mouth full. You're not worth the
candle. *Pause* Oh, Tommy . . .

SCENE TEN

*Gas Street Ragged School. Tuesday morning. It is inspection
time, and all the children — except* **Sammy** *who is
missing — are standing in rows.* **Mr Whippem,** *cane in hand,
is checking their ears, finger nails and hair, prodding hard, and
slashing their legs with his stick. As he inspects them, they sing
'We March To Our Places' — and those who have been checked,
do.*

SCRUFF KIDS We march to our places,
With clean hands and faces,
And pay great attention to all we are told.
For we know we can never,
Be happy or clever,
But learning is better, than silver or gold.
We march to our places,
With clean hands and faces,
And pay great attention, to all we are told.

At the end of the song, only **Tommy** *is left in front.* **Whippem** *gives him a sneering going-over.*

WHIPPEM   Ah, Atkins   *prod prod*   On time today, I see   *prod prod.*   And the face quite decently clean *prod prod.*   And the hair not actually alive with lice *prod prod.*   And the teeth only vaguely yellow *prod prod.*   And the breath only **almost** revolting *prod prod.*   Well done, lad. Since you gave up union militancy, I take note, you have become half-decent. Almost, indeed, fit to lick one's boots   *prod prod.*   Would you care to boy? Would you care to sully my footwear with your nasty little tongue? Well I am afraid you will not be granted the honour, young sir. For my boots, Atkins   *prod prod.*   My boots, I say   *prod prod.*   Are   *prod*   much   *prod*   too *prod*   **valuable**   *prod*   to be licked   *prod*   by the likes *prod*   of . . .

Sammy Simkins *has come in. He is standing at the door.* **Whippem** *is looking at him, with a face like thunder.*

WHIPPEM   *to* **Sammy**   You! You, boy! What is the meaning of this outrage! You are late, sir! This is a caning matter, sir! Come here, sir!   *He pushes* **Tommy** *violently towards the seated class*   And you, Atkins — sit down and shut up!

Sammy *approaches. He stands humbly in front of* **Whippem.**

WHIPPEM   Late, sir! And ill-dressed, sir! And not even wearing boots, sir! Have you no respect?

SAMMY   Please, sir, have no money, sir.

WHIPPEM   So poverty engenders lateness, does it? Lack of money makes the clock run slow, does it?

SAMMY   Please, sir, have no clock, sir. And I had to do my father's job, sir. Otherwise my mother and my sisters would starve to death, sir. Night soil collection, sir.

WHIPPEM   *leaping back a pace*   Aha! The smell! That explains it! I was too refined to mention it before, Simkins, but you reek, boy. You wear the effluvium of the sewers like an invisible aura, or mantle. In short, you stink of excrement. You are revolting, disgusting, a disgrace. Aren't you, boy? A foul, filthy, slimy, putrid insult to Gas Street Ragged School. Aren't you, boy?! Answer me!

SAMMY   Yes, sir. Sorry, sir.

WHIPPEM   What is more, pupils are expressly forbidden to allow the earning of mere money to interfere with education, as you certainly know. Starvation is better than ignorance, do you not agree? Much better!

SAMMY   Yes, sir. Indeed, sir.

WHIPPEM   Your father. Too lazy to do his own job, I suppose? On strike, I suppose, as is the fashion? Too grand to bestir himself from the bed of idleness and luxury. Well, sir? Why could your father not fulfil his functions in his chosen trade?

SAMMY   He's dead, sir. We buried him yesterday.

WHIPPEM   Hah! The lengths some people go to! A pauper's funeral, of course? Another drain upon the rates?

SAMMY   Yes, sir.

Whippem, still at arm's length or more, prods Sammy's ears with his cane, then his neck, then taps his head.

WHIPPEM   I find your excuses feeble, boy. And I find your ears clogged with dirt, your neck stained with a brownness too suggestive to be contemplated, and your hair alive with headlice. Put out your hand, boy. You will receive six strokes on the spot. And thank your lucky stars I am feeling generous this morning.

Sammy, by now, is almost broken.

SAMMY   Oh, sir. **Please** sir.

WHIPPEM   *shouts*   Your hand, Simkins!

Sammy, head hanging down, puts out his hand. Whippem holds the cane above his head, ready to swing.

TOMMY   No!

WHIPPEM   *amazed*   **What?**

TOMMY   *standing*   **No!**

WHIPPEM   *turning towards him*   **What!!**

Tommy darts forward and takes the cane. He starts to break it, fast, but deliberately.

TOMMY   That's what, you bully! That's what, you swine! That's what, you **savage!**

Whippem, shaken, stares at him.

WHIPPEM   *quietly*   Tommy Atkins, I have been waiting for this moment. You, boy, are going to pay. *He pulls back his fist* You, boy, are . . .

MARY ANN *leaping to her feet* Leave him be, you great big bully. Up, girls, up!

CHARLIE WILLIAMS *leaping to his feet* Up, lads, up!

POLLY ANDREWS Up, **class**! And **at** him!

With a cry of 'Hooray!' the class surge forward. **Whippem** *stands momentarily defiant, then runs. They chase him straight off — fast. The pupils stop at the perimeter.* **Tommy Atkins** *has leapt onto a chair.*

TOMMY *shouts* Fall in and follow me!

With a cheer, the **Kids** *form a circle round the chair. As they begin to march round they all sing.*

SCRUFF KIDS   Fall in and follow me
Fall in and follow me.
Never mind a fig about the teacher,
He can't beat yer!
Stand on me, boys, I know the way to go.
You do as I do and you'll do right.
Fall in and follow me.

They all go off, chanting: 'Down with the cane, down with the cane, down with the cane', until the area is empty.

SCENE ELEVEN

The playground at Gas Street Ragged School. A lone **Constable** *arrives, heavily disguised as a pupil. He is enormous, wears shorts and a ragged shirt, is very clean, and has policeman's highly-polished boots on. Under his school cap he is wearing a policeman's helmet, and around his neck is slung a police whistle. He goes to the centre and addresses the audience.*

CONSTABLE   Morning all. This may come as a surprise to you, but I am not what I seem. Far from being a normal subversive schoolboy on strike, I am in actual fact an undercover constabule. Mr Peel, the Chief Constabule of this 'ere borough, has hit upon this brilliant plan. I am standing here in the playground of *consults notebook* Gas Street Ragged School, waiting for the pupils to emerge. We have

25

intelligence reports, you see, that they intend to march about the borough fomenting dissent and spreading the strikes and socialistic such-likeness. Little do they expect to find me among their ranks! Imagine their amazement at my infiltration! Picture their . . . 'old 'ard! 'Ere comes one of them now! My carefully constructed subterfuge will now slip subtly into motion.

Tommy Atkins comes up to the **Constable**, *and views him with amazement. The others follow until the* **Constable** *is surrounded.*

TOMMY   'Allo, lad. Who are you? I don't know your face.

CONSTABLE   Hallo, chum. I'm the new boy. Would you like to see my conkers?

TOMMY   Conkers? In September? Gather round, friends. This is a **real** marvel.

The **Scruff Kids** *move in.*

CONSTABLE   What about this strike lark, then? Can anybody join? Oy! Give me back my cap!

Mary Ann has plucked his cap off. She tosses it in the air.

CHARLIE WILLIAMS   To me, Mary Ann! To me!

POLLY ANDREWS   Oh Grandmama! What big **boots** you have!

A game of piggy in the middle develops quickly.

TOMMY   *and a couple of the bigger boys*   All the better to **kick** you with!

The **Constable** *is kicked off. His cap is thrown after him, and his plucked-off helmet after that.*

MARY ANN   Good riddance to bad rubbish.

The **Scruff Kids** *group up and sing.*

SCRUFF KIDS   Our police are kind
Our police are gentle
Our police are good
And our police are MENTAL!

Laughing, they regroup at one end. There is an offstage clattering, and a loud shout of Huzzah! The **Constable**, *now in uniform and wielding a truncheon, charges them on an ancient boneshaker.*

CONSTABLE   Down with strikes! Down with subversion! Down with socialism!

He rides into the group, who overwhelm him and rush him straight out of the area on his bike.

ALL   Down with policemen!

CONSTABLE   *disappearing off*   Aaaaargh!

The group returns. **Mary Ann** *is holding up the policeman's trousers.*

MARY ANN   And down with policemen's trousers!

The **Scruff Kids** *group up and sing.*

SCRUFF KIDS   Our police are fat
Our police are lazy
Our police are brave
And our police are CRAZY!

SCENE TWELVE

The Town Hall. **Whippem**, **Peel**, **Baden-Powell** *and the repulsed* **Constable**, *who is trouserless.* **Whippem** *is holding a newspaper. Tableau as* **Newsboy** *speaks.*

TURN TO p.84

NEWSBOY   Read all about it, read all about it! Striking scholars demand free pencils and holidays for potato-lifting! Questions in House as fears of anarchy spread. Plain clothes policeman infiltrates strike at Gas Street — spotted! Chronicle! Rush and buy!

Whippem *hurls down the newspaper as the* **Newsboy** *leaves.*

WHIPPEM   The fact of the matter is, gentlemen, these youths have got out of hand. The example of their fathers, the moral degeneracy of the times, the falling quality of cane-wood. They have gone beyond control!

PEEL   One of my constables! Jeered at! Knocked from his bicycle! Humiliated! It is monstrous!   *The* **Constable** *weeps quietly.*   He is a broken man!

WHIPPEM   Sir Robert, with all due respect, if that man had behaved less like a milksop and more like a constable of the old school, we should not now be in the mess we are in. To be repulsed by a party of children!

27

Constable *howls.*

PEEL   A party of children is it now, Mr Whippem? If that is indeed so, how come you and your damned superior teachers were unable to control them? Young lads and girls like ravening beasts rampaging around the borough terrorising innocent policemen! What you need, sir, is less self-satisfaction and a return to the old values. Discipline and the whip!

WHIPPEM   How dare you, sir! No one — **no** one — has ever had the impertinence before to accuse me of laxity in the whippings department. If my pupils have become unmanageable it can be for one reason, and one reason only — the moral fibre of the police force is not what it was!

Constable *squalls.*

PEEL   That, sir, is the last straw. To impugn the efficiency and excellence of my boys in blue!   *Comforts* ***Constable***   There, there! There, there!   *To* **Whippem**   To **say** such things when everybody knows how lax is the discipline in Britain's schools. It is a simple outrage.

BADEN-POWELL   *stepping between them*   Gentlemen, gentlemen, desist. Control yourselves. End this unseemly bickering. There is right on both sides, but there is absolutely no point in breaking ranks. Divided we fall and all that. Pull together, men!

WHIPPEM   That is all very well, Lord Baden-Powell. All very well for you to say. But what are we to do?

PEEL   Whippem is right, BP. Keep your damned nose out if you're just going to be smug. You're not in the Army now, you know.

BADEN-POWELL   Now gentlemen, really. You talk of discipline, you talk of moral fibre. You talk of Britain's greatness. But greatness was never achieved in this way. Division of the ruling class was not what made us great. We must pull together.

WHIPPEM and **PEEL**   Yes yes! But how? All very well, etc.

BADEN-POWELL   *interrupting*   Now listen.   *To* ***Constable***   And you — stop your damned snivelling and go and find some trousers, man.   ***Constable*** *goes, still sniffling.*   Good. Now gentlemen, as you know, I was the best Boer-basher of them all. I trod the continent of Africa like a colossus. And when I returned to my dear Queen and country, I decided that the way to continued greatness was to instill the grand virtues of courage, discipline, and self-sufficiency into the young men of these sceptred isles.

PEEL   Ah yes indeed, BP. Your Boy Scouts. A useful recruiting ground for the police they'll prove, I think.

WHIPPEM   Although precious few of the Gas Street louts are members. They throw stones at them.

BADEN-POWELL   Exactly. You are both right, my friends. Now listen. In the Scouts we have a band of trained, brave, noble, clear-eyed, **tractable** young men. Who are able to use staves to great effect as an added bonus. Why don't we use 'em?

WHIPPEM   Use them? What for?

PEEL   Good God, BP, you're right! My policemen are tied up as you know in breaking real strikes, not this childish nonsense. And anyway, if they used too much force it might get in the newspapers — although I doubt it. But if . . .

BADEN-POWELL   But if my lads broke a head or two, it would all be — Good Clean British Fun . . .

WHIPPEM   Magnificent! What a splendid arrangement!

PEEL   When can they start?

BADEN-POWELL   Why not now? A short period of training, a stirring briefing, and we can set 'em on! Shall I call them in?

PEEL and **WHIPPEM**   Agreed! Agreed! Agreed!

Baden-Powell blows his whistle, and 'Land of Hope and Glory' strikes up. A contingent of Scouts march in. They are led by Cyril, and wear an odd mixture of uniforms — some in long shorts, some in khaki briefs, all with staves, neckerchiefs and hats. As Baden-Powell, Whippem and Peel stand to attention, their hands held in salutes, the Scouts march about drilling, banging into each other, knocking hats off with sticks, etc. As the music fades, they come raggedly to attention facing the leaders and saluting. Then Baden-Powell addresses them.

BADEN-POWELL   Boys, my brave boys, sons of Oldham. You, the backbone of Britain, are called upon to undertake a sacred and a perilous duty. As you may have heard, there is a black-hearted plot afoot to overthrow the rule of law in our beloved city. An army of double-dyed villains, scum and the progeny of scum to a boy and girl, have sworn to bring the blood and terror of revolution, red-hot and dripping, to this quiet backwater of the Empire . . .

*From about halfway through this, 'Land of Hope and Glory' has struck up, and got louder until **Baden-Powell** is drowned, although he goes on, mouthing and gesticulating frantically. At last the **Scouts** give a mighty cheer, and march off. **Baden-Powell**, **Whippem** and **Peel** march after them. Music fades.*

SCENE THIRTEEN

*The Atkins' home. **Tommy** and **Mrs Atkins** are having a row.*

TOMMY But you said it yourself, Mum — it's the principle of the thing! They've treated us like muck, the headmaster was going to whip Sammy Simkins just for being dirty, and then they set the police on us! They can't treat us like that and they shouldn't!

MRS ATKINS I said it was the principle of the thing for grown men, not for silly kids. Your father had a real grievance.

TOMMY We've got a real grievance. It's 'orrible in school. It shouldn't happen to a dog, what they make us suffer.

MRS ATKINS Suffer! Tommy Atkins, you make me sick! Do you know that half the working men in this country earn less than twenty-five shillings a week for working nearly sixty hours! Do you know there are hundreds upon hundreds of people, in this town alone, who haven't got a roof over their heads? Do you know there are five families in this street whose children have never worn a pair of shoes?

TOMMY Do you know that Gas Street School's got five hundred kids in it and only four classrooms? Do you know there's only one headmaster and seven other assistant teachers? Do you know the monitors do all the work for **nothing**?

MRS ATKINS It doesn't matter, Tommy, it's not **real**. It may be hard, it may be awful, but the real world's worse. And if you don't get your attendance in, and a good report — you'll never even **hope** to get a proper job. Nobody will touch you.

TOMMY My father had a proper job, and look what

happened to him. He had to go on strike. He's in prison. And you said he might never work again.

MRS ATKINS   If you strike, Tommy, you might never get the chance to work at all. They'll be watching, Tommy, don't you understand? They'll be taking names. The people in control won't let themselves forget. Not never.

The storm has passed. They sit in silence.

TOMMY   *at last*   My father's stuck in jail, for fighting for his rights. And I might never work.

MRS ATKINS   Yes, Tommy. That's what I'm afraid of.

TOMMY   But does that mean we should give in, Mum? Does it? Honestly.

MRS ATKINS   *after pause*   Tommy, you are not your father. The summer's hot, and school's boring. But you are not your father.

TOMMY   So you think I should give in?

MRS ATKINS   *after pause*   Tommy, love. You are not your father . . .

SCENE FOURTEEN

The Fanshawe's home. **Mr Fanshawe** *is reading a newspaper.* **Mrs Fanshawe** *and* **Cynthia** *are sewing. Tableau as* **Newsboy** *shouts.*

NEWSBOY   Read all about it! Socialists infect Newcastle scholars! Shock demand for more holidays and a penny to be given to all pupils every Friday! Flying pickets at Islington intimidate good boys and smash school windows! Buy your Chronicle now!

MR FANSHAWE   *coming out of tableau as* **Newsboy** *leaves*   Amazing. A week ago I would not have thought it possible. These school strikes are everywhere. There is hardly a part of our united isles that has not become infected.

MRS FANSHAWE   I blame it on the parents. I blame it on the teachers. There is no respect for authority any more — not a jot.

MR FANSHAWE   There is no doubt in my mind at all, my

dear. These strikes are manifestations of a serious degeneration in the moral fibre of the rising generations.

MRS FANSHAWE   Lack of discipline — that is the root of it, Charles. They need whipping — hard, long and often.

MR FANSHAWE   Spare the rod and spoil the child. Thus saith the Good Book. And rarely has a truer word been written.

MRS FANSHAWE   It is the aftermath that worries me particularly, dear. The school authorities must weed out the ringleaders at least. The bad apples must be plucked from the barrel before all are infected.

MR FANSHAWE   My worry, dearest, is that the moral contamination is already there. In short that there are no ringleaders — merely a whole barrelfull of rotten fruit. A whole generation of snakes and serpents. A whole class in our beloved nation of traitors and worse.

CYNTHIA   But Daddy, surely they can't **all** be bad. Gas Street Ragged School, for instance. Conditions there are . . .

Her mother has stood, and is now facing her.

MRS FANSHAWE   What?! What did you dare to say, Miss?! Do my ears **deceive** me, child!?

CYNTHIA   I'm sorry, mother, but I truly think . . .

Her father is now facing her also.

MR FANSHAWE   How **dare** you, girl! How **dare** you! Have you been contaminated? What exactly are you saying?

CYNTHIA   Only, Papa, that . . .

MRS FANSHAWE   Oh Charles! We have bred a viper in our bosom! A traitor. A . . . a . . . a . . . **socialist**!

CYNTHIA   Nonsense, mother. I think the strikes are . . .

MR FANSHAWE   Nonsense!? You dare to use a word like that to your mother! Out! Out of this room! Out of my sight!

CYNTHIA   But Papa!

MR FANSHAWE   To your room, Miss! Instantly!

CYNTHIA   Mama!

MRS FANSHAWE   Do not speak to me, Cynthia. Unless it is to apologise. Go to your room this instant. And prepare yourself for some punishment.

CYNTHIA *going* Punishment? Oh Papa, Mama. You would not, surely . . . ?

MR FANSHAWE *declaiming* Withhold not correction from the child; For if thou . . .

Cynthia bumps into Cyril, who has just entered. He is in Scout uniform, and dementedly excited.

CYNTHIA Oh! Oh — Cyril.

CYRIL Pater! Mater! We've got a spiffing wheeze! We're going to attack the strikers! We're going to beat them silly! We're going to drive them back to school!

MRS FANSHAWE Oh **Cyril**. At least you are still my darling!

MR FANSHAWE **That's** the spirit, son. Cynthia — you may go to bed.

But she has gone.

SCENE FIFTEEN

*The Simkins' home. **Sammy** is preparing to go to the pawnshop. In front of him is a small bundle of rags, a blanket, some shawls. He is wearing a shirt and shorts.*

MRS SIMKINS Don't fret, Sammy. Perhaps we'll be able to redeem them before winter. And the girls certainly don't need their shawls in this weather, do they?

SAMMY Nor the blanket for their bed. But it will be October soon, Mum. Three weeks or less.

MRS SIMKINS Maybe it will be a mild winter, love. At least they've got each other to make a bit of heat. You have to sleep on your own, poor boy.

SAMMY If they keep me on at Dad's job I'll be working all night anyway. When I go to bed it's daytime. Always warmer then. And there's usually a bit of fire at school.

MRS SIMKINS Yes, school's a blessing. These terrible bad boys, who are out on strike. Biting the hand that feeds them. Mocking authority. No good can come of it, no good at all.

SAMMY *uncomfortable* I'd better go now, Mum. The pawnshop might close.

MRS SIMKINS *small laugh* The pawnshop never closes, Sammy. Here — take this.

She takes off her thin shawl and holds it out.

SAMMY Mum. No. It's all you've got, you'll freeze.

MRS SIMKINS You'd never join the strikers, would you Sammy? You wouldn't be a bad lad?

She presses the shawl into his hands. **Sammy** *is looking at the ground.*

SAMMY No Mum. Of course I wouldn't.

Enter **Newsboy**.

NEWSBOY School strikes still spreading! Several thousand roam the streets of Dundee! Teacher hit on head with brickbat! Police and pedagogues wade in! Read all about it! Buy your Evening Chron!

SCENE SIXTEEN

P. 79 TURN TO

Outside the Mumps Academy. **Scruff Kids** *picketing, led by* **Tommy Atkins**. *They are carrying placards: 'Join the Strike', 'Fall in and follow us', 'Even Posh Kids can fight', etc. They are chanting.*

SCRUFF KIDS No more work, no more cane
Or we won't go back again.
No more work, no more cane
Or we won't go back again!

The **Narrator** *steps forward, grandly. He holds up his hand for silence. The chant stops.*

NARRATOR *pompously* Thank you.

SCRUFF KIDS *chant* Silence at the front!
Silence at the back!
Pin back your dirty lug'oles,
While he opens up his trap!

NARRATOR Charming I am sure, ladies and gentlemen. Perhaps now you have an inkling of the depths to which the Lower Orders of this country have sunk. And I can only report, in all solemnity, that what you have heard of this disgraceful business so far, is true. By mid-September, no

34

fewer than sixty-two towns or areas were involved. There
was Ancoats, Ardwick, Ashton. Cheetham, Colchester,
Cardiff. Sheffield, Stockport and Stoke. Grantham, Grimsby,
Galashiels and Glasgow, London, Llanelly, Leeds and
Liverpool. Dublin was down, with Dumbarton, Derby and
Darlington. Birkenhead, of course, and Bradford. And
Barrow, and Brum, with Bristol, Blyth and Burton.
Halifax . . .

SCRUFF KIDS *roaring* Why don't you **shut up**!

NARRATOR And at Oldham, ladies and gentlemen, the
children of Gas Street Ragged were doing their worst. *He
puts on a smug smile* Why, then, do I smile? I smile, ladies
and gentlemen, for what fate holds in store for them. On this
sunny September morning the Scouts are not even a faint
cloud on the horizon of their minds. But we have seen them
training, you and I, and may tremble. For soon: Tommy
Atkins and Co. will meet their Waterloo!

*As the **Narrator** withdraws, **Sammy Simkins** walks past the
picket, trying not to be seen. He is wearing only a pair of
shorts — all he has left. **Tommy** spots him.*

TOMMY Sam! Sammy! Where you going, lad?

*Sammy tries to dart out. **Mary Ann** grabs him.*

MARY ANN *holding her nose* Ooh, what a pong!

TOMMY Leave him be. *To **Sammy*** You been to work?
Come and join the picket. We're going to get the Mumps
Academy lot to join in.

SAMMY I can't. I'm going back to school.

TOMMY You what? Going back.

MARY ANN and **CHARLIE WILLIAMS** He's a dirty
blackleg.

SCRUFF KIDS *chant* Sammy is a blackleg, Sammy is a
blackleg.

TOMMY *shouts* Shut up! Leave him be! What's going on,
Sammy? What are you talking about?

SAMMY It's my M . . . It's . . . It's nothing. I've just got to,
that's all. I can't risk my job. I might get the sack. They
might find out.

TOMMY But Sammy! United we stand! You know that!

SAMMY It's all right for you, Tom. You ain't . . .

SCRUFF KIDS *seeing the Mumps girls approach* Here come the poshies! Here come the poshies! Here come the poshies!

As Cynthia, Lily and other posh girls approach, Sammy takes his opportunity. He sneaks off. The Scruff Kids form a picket line.

LILY Let us pass, you horrid lot.

TOMMY We're asking you nicely. Will you join the strike?

The girls laugh in a nasty upper crust way.

GIRL 1 Oh! Isn't he quaint!

GIRL 2 That accent! Marvellous!

GIRL 3 And those **extraordinary** trousers!

POLLY ANDREWS We've got legitimate grievances, you know.

Laughter as before.

LILY Oh I say! Legitimate whatties?

GIRL 1 She can almost speak **English**!

GIRL 2 **Grievances**! Oh Cynthia! Have you ever **heard** such a thing!

Cynthia has said nothing. She is embarrassed.

LILY Come on, girls. Time for school.

TOMMY *as they approach the line* Please. It would make it much more . . . respectable.

GIRLS Respectable! Oh, isn't he killing! Oh those trousers, etc.

MARY ANN *brandishing fist* And if you try to bust our line, we'll bust your noses. So there!

Girls twitter in fright.

TOMMY No, let 'em through, Mary Ann. If we can't persuade 'em — let them through.

The picket line parts — jeering. The posh girls carefully pick their way through. Tommy speaks to Cynthia, slightly apart.

TOMMY Won't you join us, Cynthia?

CYNTHIA No. I can't. I think you're . . . I think it's . . .

LILY *calling back* Cynthia, what are you doing?! You're not talking to one of them!?

CYNTHIA No! I . . .

She makes to go.

TOMMY We're going down the Sands tomorrow. Royton Sands. Are you coming?

LILY Cynthia!

TOMMY We'll be meeting at Pick Hill. About ten. You'd be very welcome.

LILY Cynthia! Come **on**!

CYNTHIA Coming! No, look, I . . . *Hisses* Look — you're about to be attacked. I'm warning you. Get moving, quickly. You're going to be attacked!

*Lily marches up and grabs **Cynthia**.*

TOMMY You what? We're what?

LILY Cynthia Fanshawe, what **are** you thinking of? Stop talking to that dirty boy and come inside at once.

TOMMY *as **Cynthia** starts to move* Cynthia . . .

LILY Oh! Do you **know** him, Cynthia?

CYNTHIA Of course I don't. *To **Tommy*** How dare you speak to me like that! How dare you!

Tommy is speechless as the girls run through the line and disappear.

TOMMY Oh to hell with you. To hell with all the lot of you.

*The **Scruff Kids** cluster round him.*

MARY ANN Do you know her, Tommy Atkins? Do you know that stuck-up little . . .

TOMMY Sssh! What's that! What's that noise?

*Off, we hear the strains of 'Land of Hope and Glory'. Starting very low, it swells quickly to a crescendo. **Sammy Simkins** comes rushing on. He goes to **Tommy**.*

SAMMY It's the Scouts! They're coming! They're going to attack us!

TOMMY Us? I thought you'd given up.

SAMMY I couldn't, could I? I watched from round the corner. I saw the way them posh girls treated us. Can I join in again?

TOMMY   Brother — shake.

As they shake hands, the **Scouts** *appear, with staves and shields and rope. They form up into a military-type platoon, with* **Cyril** *at their head. The* **Scruff Kids** *form up and face them.*

SCRUFF KIDS   *chant*   Here come the Brussels Sprouts
   The dirty lot of louts,
   With dustbin lids and broomsticks,
   Here come the Brussels Sprouts.

CYRIL   We'll wipe the smiles off your dirty little faces, you scruffy weak-kneed lot. One! Two! Three! Charge!!!

The **Scouts** *charge, possibly in slow motion. The* **Scruff Kids** *— without a fight — absorb the* **Scouts** *into the ruck. From out of it fly hats, neckerchiefs, shields, etc. Then — suddenly — amid a lot of noise, the ruck breaks up and the* **Scouts** *are chased wildly off and away. As everyone disappears, the* **Narrator** *comes on.*

NARRATOR   The cheek of them. The infernal impudence. First they dare to picket the young gentleladies of the Mumps Academy, then they rout the forces of law and order embodied by Baden-Powell's boys. In mid-September, ladies and gentlemen, the time had come. Mr Whippem, Lord BP, and Sir Robert Peel sought advice. From authority. From the highest authority in the land. Ladies and gentlemen — the Queen!

SCENE SEVENTEEN

To the strains of 'God Save the Queen', **Victoria** *— as before — is trundled into view. From the other end of the area,* **Whippem**, **Peel** *and* **Baden-Powell** *grovel in, bowing like automata. They range themselves in front of her. At last she points to* **Whippem**.

WHIPPEM   *going up to her*   Your Majesty. Joshua Whippem, headmaster.

He puts his head to hers. Whispering noises.

WHIPPEM   *walking away backwards*   Thank you, Ma'am. Indeed thank you.

Queen *points to* **Peel**.

PEEL *going to her* Your Majesty. Sir Robert Peel. Chief of the Oldham Constabulary.

Heads together. Whispers.

PEEL *walking backwards* Thank you, Ma'am. Your ever so humble subject.

Queen *points to* **Baden-Powell**.

BADEN-POWELL Your Majesty. Lord Baden-Powell Reliever of Lady Smith.

Heads together. Whispers.

BADEN-POWELL *walking backwards* Thank you, Ma'am. Wonderful advice. The schoolboy strikes, as I have always maintained, are in reality something of a joke.

THE QUEEN *if she is a dummy, her bewigged attendant can say this* We . . . are . . . not . . . amused.

'God Save the Queen' strikes up. As **Victoria** *is trundled off, waving regally,* **Baden-Powell**, **Peel** *and* **Whippem** *scrape out backwards, bowing as before. When she has gone and they are almost off, they stop.*

WHIPPEM Why did **we** not think of that? The simplicity!

PEEL What a woman! What a wonderful plan!

BADEN-POWELL Every inch a queen. She has given us an **invincible** Secret Weapon . . .

ALL God save her majesty!

SCENE EIGHTEEN

Pick Hill. The **Scruff Kids** *gather for their trip out in the sun.* **Sammy**, *in his shorts, is darting among them, trying to improvise a charabanc.*

SAMMY Come on, Polly. You can be the driver if you like. No point in going to the seaside if you go on foot. We need a chara.

CHARLIE WILLIAMS You're cracked you are, Sammy. How can we make a motor coach? We're only a bunch of kids.

SAMMY   We can do anything if we try hard enough. That's what my old Dad used to say.

MARY ANN   Aye. And look where it got him!

POLLY ANDREWS   Sammy's right, it's easy. First of all we need the seats. Who'll be the seats? Then some wheels, and possibly an engine. Come on, let's be having you! Tommy! Come over here!

Tommy, who has been standing aloof, glancing off from time to time, ignores her. The other kids start to turn themselves into a small motor coach.

MARY ANN   *close to Sammy*   Heh up, Sam. You're smelling sweet today. Is everything coming up roses for you at last?

SAMMY   No. I lost my job and had a wash. They've given me the sack.

MARY ANN   Never! What for?! Was it for joining in the strike?

SAMMY   No. They never found that out. The boss just decided they could do without me, that's all. Save themselves three bob.

MARY ANN   But there weren't enough of you anyway, were there? They worked you like a dog. Didn't the others complain?

TOMMY   They didn't dare. In case they got similar.

MARY ANN   All for a measly three bob. It weren't enough to live on anyway.

SAMMY   I know. But it's three shillings worth of extra jam a week for the boss, ain't it? And for me — well — I don't stink no more! Until I starve to death and rot, that is. Me and my Mum and sisters.

MARY ANN   You don't seem to care that much.

SAMMY   Don't I, Mary Ann? *Pause*   Well — that's a mercy, isn't it?

CHARLIE WILLIAMS   *calling from the chara*   Come on, you two! Come on, Tommy Atkins! We're ready for the off.

Mary Ann takes Sammy's hand and they skip to the chara. Tommy hangs back at the perimeter.

POLLY ANDREWS   Tommy! Hurry **up**!

Tommy shakes his head miserably, as the Scruff Kids start to sing, punctuating their singing with hooting horns.

SCRUFF KIDS   Oh we're off,   *parp parp*   we're off,   *parp parp*
      We're off in a motor car!
      Sixty bobbies are after us
      And we don't know where we are!
      Oh we're off,   *parp parp*   we're off,   *parp parp*
      We're off in a motor car!
      Sixty bobbies are after us
      And we don't know where we are!

With a cheer and engine noises, the kids 'drive' or stream off. Tommy is left alone. Cynthia appears behind him.

CYNTHIA   Tommy. Have they gone? Am I too late to go to Royton Sands?

TOMMY   Cynthia! Oh, whizz **oh**! Hell, Cynthia! Come on, hurry! If we run, we might just catch the chara! Hurry!

She runs towards him. He grabs her hand, and they race off after the others. Off, we hear, sung quite softly.

SCRUFF KIDS   Beavers, Bulldogs, sitting on a wall —
      Selling horse muck, penny a ball.
      Parp parp!

SCENE NINETEEN

Peel, Whippem and Baden-Powell. Cyril comes panting up to them.

BADEN-POWELL   Well, Cyril. What news?

WHIPPEM   I am not sure, gentlemen, that I approve of spying. It is not entirely honourable. Or British.

PEEL   I agree entirely, Whippem. It is entirely repugnant. Unless one needs the information, of course.

BADEN-POWELL   Naturally. And Cyril is my best man. What news, boy?

CYRIL   Please, sir. They've gone to Royton Sands. All of them. The lower classes. And . . . and . . . and my sister Cynthia, sir.

PEEL   Good God! Doesn't she attend the Mumps Academy?

CYRIL   Yes sir.

WHIPPEM   And is your father not a magistrate?

CYRIL   Yes sir.

BADEN-POWELL   *head in hands*   That is appalling! Oh gentlemen, the very fabric of society is crumbling.

WHIPPEM   Then, Baden-Powell, it is time to act. We must mobilise all our forces. And we must use the Secret Weapon suggested by the Queen. Now!

PEEL   We must, gentlemen. Indeed we must.

*As they leave, the **Newsboy** comes on.*

NEWSBOY   Read all about it! Read all about it! Westerly wind experienced in Cornwall. Clouds spotted on horizon! Precipitation possible soon. Temperature dropping on the Coast. Buy your Chronicle! Read your Evening Chron!

SCENE TWENTY

*The corner shop. **Mrs Atkins** is standing at the counter, and **Mrs Simkins** is behind her.*

SHOPKEEPER   One loaf, a quarter of tea, a pound of fish and two eggs. That's one and tuppence please, Mrs Atkins.

MRS ATKINS   Could you put it on the slate, Mrs T?

SHOPKEEPER   Mrs Atkins. I told you yesterday and I meant it. You owe thirteen shillings and thruppence farthing. Until you have paid some of it off, there is no more slate.

MRS ATKINS   My boy must eat, Mrs T.

SHOPKEEPER   And drink tea, I suppose? I run a shop, Mrs Atkins, not a friendly society.

MRS ATKINS   The full amount will be paid in time. I have never let you down. It is only credit, Mrs T.

SHOPKEEPER   You must learn to live within your means now. You should not need to borrow.

MRS ATKINS   Just the bread then. And one egg?

SHOPKEEPER   No, Mrs Atkins. Nothing.   *To Mrs Simkins*   Can I help you, Mrs Simkins?

MRS SIMKINS *watching **Mrs Atkins** replace goods* No . . . I. No thank you, Mrs T. I wasn't thinking. I should be in the Post Office. I'm going daft.

Shopkeeper *exits. The two women look at each other, in the street.*

MRS ATKINS I've got a small half-loaf at home love. Would you like to share it?

MRS SIMKINS *bitterly* I don't want charity from the likes of you. Troublemakers! It's your sort that's got me in this mess.

MRS ATKINS Troublemakers? Whatever can you mean?

MRS SIMKINS A striking jailbird for a husband. Putting you and your family in poverty and hardship out of pure greed. Upsetting them with money so that they turn against us poor. You know what I mean.

MRS ATKINS We've got to fight, Mrs Simkins. We've got to stand up for our rights.

MRS SIMKINS Rights! We've got no rights! All I've got between me and death is my boy and his job. And your Tommy's been causing trouble at the school. I know. All this striking nonsense. Thank God my Sammy's got more sense, that's all. He'll keep his job, Mrs Atkins — poor job as it is. He ain't going to join no coddled hotheads.

MRS ATKINS I hope my boy's not on strike. I've told him what I . . .

MRS SIMKINS Thank God the bosses play it fair, that's all. And thank God my Sammy's got more sense than some. He'll keep his job, missus, just you see. Then **you'll** come begging, maybe. You and your dirty charity and your dirty bread.

She stalks off.

MRS ATKINS *quietly* Poor Mrs Simkins.

SCENE TWENTY-ONE

Royton Sands. There is a brass band playing, off. Two of the **Scruff Kids** *have dressed up as a donkey, with cardboard ears, to give rides. A girl has filled her clothes with cushions and is standing near a Guess My Weight placard. Others are juggling, others doing acrobatics, another is dressed as a boxer, sparring* *air. A few are just lying stretched out, as if sunbathing.* **Tommy** *and* **Cynthia** *stroll round, hand in hand.*

VARIOUS CRIES   Roll up! Roll up! Guess the fat lady's weight and win a kiss!

Donkey rides! Donkey rides! Farthing a go. There and back again to see how far it is!

Go two rounds with the Bradford Bruiser! Win two fag cards and a mouthful of corporation pop!

Challenge the strong man, challenge the strong man! Hold him above your head for five minutes with one hand and win a thousand pounds!

CYNTHIA   *looking at the sunbathers who are fully clothed and apparently dead*   What are they doing, Tommy?

TOMMY   They're playing Blackpool. Is it like that really?

CYNTHIA   Well, people do just lie there, doing nothing, it's true.

TOMMY   There you are then.

CYNTHIA   Yes. I suppose I am.

They walk on a while.

TOMMY   Cynthia. I know it's not Blackpool really, all this. But . . . but . . . do you like it? Are you glad you came?

CYNTHIA   Tommy, I . . .

TOMMY   Ooh look! The Pierrots!

All the **Scruff Kids** *form up quickly in the centre to sing.*

SCRUFF KIDS   Me and the wife and the family of three
Went to Royton-by-the-Sea.
We watched clog dancers
And we listened to the band —
Then we played on Royton Sands.

A **gingerbread seller** *comes on with a tray. Everyone takes some, quickly.*

SCRUFF KIDS   We kept eating parkin (parkin!)
We kept eating parkin (parkin!)
We kept eating parkin
That's why we are so brown!

TOMMY   Do you like parkin, Cynthia?

CYNTHIA   Tommy, I like everything. It's better than

Blackpool, honestly. It's a hundred, thousand, **million** times better than Blackpool. It's **wonderful**.

*Everybody becomes very quiet. As **Tommy** and **Cynthia** lean towards each other, very very slowly, for a chaste kiss. But as their lips are about to meet, the **Narrator**, who has arrived unnoticed, speaks.*

NARRATOR   Aah, isn't that beautiful, ladies and gentlemen. Next he'll be making a speech.

***Tommy** springs away from **Cynthia** onto a box. All the **Scruff Kids** spring into position in front of him and form an audience.*

TOMMY   Well lads and lasses, here we are. And well lads and lasses, this is it! We're out on strike, and we're going to win. No more caning, no more Latin verbs, no more being pushed around by stuck up prigs of assistant teachers in polished boots. Here we'll sit, and lap up the sun. We're out on strike, the rest of the country's out on strike, and out we'll all stay till they meet our demands! They'll pay us, maybe. Or cut our hours. Or abolish the cane. We'll have **real** education, without drudgery and beatings!

SAMMY   Hooray, that's the spirit, friends. We'll stick it out together!

TOMMY   Aye. Solidarity is the watchword, lads and lasses. We've turned up trumps because we've stuck together, just like our Dads have done. It'll spread now; it's bound to. It's all over this country, and why not? Today Gas Street — tomorrow the world!

*There is a pandemonium of cheering, and in the confusion **Tommy** and **Cynthia** may have their kiss. But the **Narrator** strides forward, braying through a megaphone.*

NARRATOR   Enough, you fools. Enough, you children. Stop this ridiculous celebrating at once. The fun is finished, the carousel has run its course. You may do battle, or you may come quietly. That is up to you. I hereby present the Opposition. Now — be silent.

*The **Scruff Kids** move to one side. The **Narrator** takes up a commanding position. Using a pointer, he draws up the battle lines.*

NARRATOR   Ladies and gentlemen: the Battle of Royton

Sands. May I present to you, the Front Rank. Please cheer the forces of law and order.

Peel, *Whippem* and *Baden-Powell* enter, followed by a fearful *Constable* on his bike. The *Scruff Kids* boo.

WHIPPEM   Boo your worst, little ones. The end, for you, is in sight.

NARRATOR   Ladies and gentlemen — the Second Rank.

The *Scouts*, *in bandages, wheelchairs and on crutches, come forward. The* *Scruff Kids* *cheer.*

CYRIL   We'll show you this time, you rotters. This time we're prepared!

NARRATOR   Ladies and gentlemen. A touch of reality.

The *Newsboy* *enters. Carrying a raised umbrella.*

NEWSBOY   *sneezes*   Heavy and continuous rain was today reported to be spreading to all parts of the British Isles. The drought is over.

NARRATOR   Now. Let battle commence.

TOMMY   We'll never surrender!

SAMMY   We'll beat you in the end!

CYNTHIA   United we stand, divided we . . .

PEEL   Right, you scallywags, you asked for it. Unveil the Secret Weapon!

Off, music strikes up. First two lines are sung off, then the *Mums* *— in turbans, aprons, shawls, rags — come streaming in, singing powerfully. They are led by* *Mrs Simkins*.

MUMS   We're the Mums of Oldham Town,
We're the Mums of Great Renown,
Known to every silly clown,
In the city boundary!

Some of the *Scruff Kids*, *knowing they are defeated, begin to slip off. Some* *Mums* *break ranks and grip them — by the arms, ears, anything. The singing becomes grimmer.*

MUMS   All those silly little lads,
Gone on strike just like their Dads,
Soon they'll wish they never had —
When their bums are smarting!

*As the **Kids** try to run, the first verse is repeated. The **Kids** race about but cannot escape. Harrassed by **Peel**, **Whippem**, **Baden-Powell**, **Constable** and **Scouts**, they are caught in every corner of the area by their **Mums** — cuffed, kicked and clipped. They are taken off, and become totally silent. **Sammy Simkins** remains hidden, **Tommy** and **Cynthia** also remain. Everybody else has left, except **Mrs Simkins**. She looks about until she spots her son.*

MRS SIMKINS Sammy Simkins, you've let me down. Come quickly now, in case somebody sees you and you lose your job. You'll get nowhere, you won't, if you don't treat certain people with respect. Keep acting up like this, Sammy Simkins, and you'll be the death of me.

*Sammy comes slowly out. When he has almost reached her he turns to **Tommy**.*

SAMMY Tom, I've . . .

MRS SIMKINS Don't you talk to him, Sammy. He's an evil influence. You come home with me. It's time you got ready to go to work.

SAMMY *as they leave* Yes, mother.

*Mrs Atkins walks slowly in from one end. Before she reaches **Tommy**, **Mr and Mrs Fanshawe** arrive from the other end.*

MRS ATKINS Tommy.

MR FANSHAWE You disgusting girl! Unhand that filthy person. Come to my side immediately, child.

CYNTHIA Papa.

MRS FANSHAWE One more word, Miss, and you leave our family. The gutter will be your home.

CYNTHIA Mama.

MR FANSHÀWE One more word.

*Off, a gentle reprise of 'Dont Touch My Silk Dress'. **Cynthia** looks at **Tommy**, lets go of his hand, and follows her parents off. When they are gone, **Mrs Atkins** speaks.*

MRS ATKINS Your father will be out of prison soon, Tommy. *Pause* He will be proud of you.

*The music ends. **Tommy** is alone.*

SCENE TWENTY-TWO

*Enter **Newsboy**. Oilskins and umbrella.*

NEWSBOY   Read all about it! Rain lashes Britain, teachers
lash pupils. Headmasters vie for superiority in wielding
cane. Strikers struck in Swansea, London louts leathered,
Birkenhead boys beaten black and blue. Get your Evening
Chronicle, get your Chronicle here!

*The **Narrator** walks on as the **Newsboy** walks off. He
approaches **Tommy** and puts his hand on his shoulder.*

NARRATOR   Well Tommy, what did you expect? It was only
summer madness after all. You Lower Classes did not expect
to be taken seriously, surely not? Maybe the classrooms are
overcrowded and the lessons stupid. Maybe the punishments
are appalling and the teachers worse. But who are you to
complain — or even judge? You are not experts on the
educational system, you are only guinea pigs, or victims.
And consider — if you do not win an attendance medal, you
may not win a job. If you gain a report for being independent,
you may gain a name for being awkward. It is docility that is
required of you, Tommy Atkins, not the infernal arrogance
to think and question. We want you to grow to manhood
quietly — and go into the wider world prepared. Prepared
for what is needed of you by your country.

*As the cast begin to come on, some almost marching, all
sombrely, the strains of 'Keep the Home Fires Burning' can be
heard. The **Narrator** starts to give **Tommy** the 'trappings of
manhood' — a khaki jacket, a tin hat, a rifle. The music slowly
swells.*

NARRATOR   You may not be able to read or write, Tommy
Atkins. You may not be able to add up. But at least you will
be hungry and cowed. Hungry and cowed enough to join the
Army in 1914 — which is only, after all, just around the
corner. Hungry and cowed enough to fight, and to bleed, and
to suffer.

***Tommy** is now dressed as a soldier. The cast are humming the
tune.*

NARRATOR   And after that, Tommy Atkins, there is a
country fit for heroes to come back to.

48

If you come back a hero.

If you come back.

In the meantime, Tommy. Well — summer's over, isn't it. It will be October soon. It's chilly, in the rain. And it's getting chillier. Think of it, Tommy. There'll be a fire in school tomorrow, maybe.

At least there's a fire on in school.

The cast sing 'Keep the Home Fires Burning', and the music reaches a crescendo.

Performing The Rebels of Gas Street

The Rebels of Gas Street is a play of action. A good production will need clearly defined characters and well co-ordinated groupwork. The strikes had all the physical energy, spontaneity and imagination of street play and these qualities should be reflected in the performance, so beware the deadpan effect that can occur when reading the text in a group. In scenes with lots of characters and action — the classroom, playground, Royton Sands — you may find it easier to put the text to one side and develop the drama through improvisation.

Characters
The variety of characters in the play calls for different acting styles. The poor families and the Scruff Kids, generally the most human characters in the play, speak and interact naturalistically. By contrast, the Fanshawes and authority figures are generally stereotypes or cardboard cut-outs. A cartoonist would express them by selecting one or two key physical attributes, e.g. nose or ears, and then exaggerating them. The same can be done in drama.

It helps to add some descriptive words to the process. So, Queen Victoria may be a 'pompous nose', Baden-Powell a 'proud chest', Mr Whippem a 'fierce eye-brows' character. The key physical feature of the character should affect posture, walk and speech.

Practise entrances and exits to draw out the contrast between these characters. This exercise will then lead naturally into the opening scene in which the narrator introduces each authority figure in turn. You may choose not to have anybody playing Queen Victoria, and to represent her by means of a cardboard cut-out. This would present no problems, even in Scene Seventeen where her attendant could say the one line required there.

Groupwork
Group scenes such as the scragging of Sammy Simkins and the picketing outside The Mumps Academy are best created spontaneously. However, there are other scenes where you could gain special effect by carefully choreographing movement, sound and speech. In each case you should try to build a clear dramatic image that conveys the *essence* of the feeling or attitude appropriate to the scene, e.g. the Scruff Kids snoring in unison at the beginning of Scene Two.

Space
Though the play could be performed in the classroom, it would probably work better in a hall (or drama studio if you have one), especially if you want to use a large cast. If possible, avoid jamming all the scenes on to the stage behind a proscenium arch. It would be a good idea to put the main action on the floor of the auditorium close to the audience. This would involve raising the rear rows of seating to give clear sightlines on the action. If you have insufficient rostra for this purpose, the simplest solution would be to put the audience on, and in front

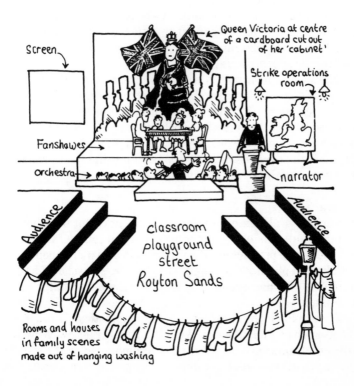

of, the stage; but a more effective arrangement would be to have audience on both sides of the action. This would allow you to give each group in the play its own 'territory' and to emphasise the high status of the Fanshawes and the authorities by placing them on the stage (see diagram).

Bear in mind the need for wide exits and entrances and circulation space behind. These facilitate the flow of actors around the space and draw the audience into the action. For example, the drilling of the scouts or the fights and chases, could take place in and around the audience, perhaps even involving some of the audience as scouts or policemen.

The most difficult scene changes are those from outside to inside the school and vice versa. The action would flow more smoothly if you used chairs only for the classroom. (This idea offers dramatic possibilities for hiding/playing/passing messages behind invisible desk lids.)

Above all, when designing the lay-out, look carefully at your performance space to see how its particular dimensions and features might be used to advantage.

Slide projection screen

A slide projection screen would enable you to incorporate information and pictures into the action, e.g. newspaper headlines, information on temperature and weather, photographs of strikers, etc.

The speed with which the strikes spread across the country could be demonstrated by showing on the screen the places where strikes were happening and the numbers of strikers involved when these facts are called out by the Newsboy. An alternative method would be to create a Strike Operations Room with operators or the Newsboy marking the towns that fall victim to the strike epidemic on a large map of England.

Music

Music is a vital element in the play. The narrator is rather like a music-hall master of ceremonies, and you could, if you wish, set the whole production in a music-hall. The more people involved in playing and singing the better. The school band, if you have one, has a ready-made role as the music-hall orchestra.

Try to exploit the contrast between 'sophisticated' music-hall songs such as Lily's 'Daddy Wouldn't Buy Me a Bow-Wow' and the street songs and strike chants accompanied by the street orchestra of tin-whistles, combs and paper, and saucepan lids.

FINDING STORIES IN YOUR OWN LOCALITY

The next section provides resource material for you to work on alongside the play. It contains pictures, stories and reports about social conditions and school strikes from many parts of the country. Stories from the area where you live would add a special flavour to the drama, but to find them you will probably need to do some research of your own. Here are some ways of setting about it.

1   Look through the 1911 issues of your local newspaper for reports of strike action. You should be able to find these in the newspaper offices or the reference section of your town library. If no strikes took place in your area, the papers will certainly provide other information about local characters and events which you could build into your improvisations. (The women's section and the vicar's column usually make fascinating reading.)

2   Visit a school that was the scene of strike action. Talk to the present headmaster about the history of the school and look up reports in the school logbook. (Many of these will now be stored in local libraries.)

3   Contact your local history society and the schools museum service. They may have old photographs, costumes, objects and information which could help you to get the feeling of life in your area in 1911. Collect local songs and rhymes — those that refer to people and places you know will be especially useful.

4   *Talk to old people.* All the stories in the next section were collected recently from old people who were born around the beginning of the century. Memories of childhood remain vivid into old age and most people enjoy sharing them. They could be your most valuable source of information.

Allow the stories you collect to alter the characters and structure of the play. You may, for example, find a new Tommy

Atkins figure, or you may wish to replace Tommy with a girl strike leader.

5 Finally, look at your own school today. Enlist the help of your teachers in examining various aspects of school life. Though you are very familiar with school, many of its features probably remain a mystery to you — the reasons behind what is being taught, school rules, etc. If the idea of adapting the play appeals to you, consider the possibilities of combining the historical with a contemporary setting. What would it be like if pupils today met pupils from 1911? Do you think they would be able to learn anything from each other?

Resource Material

Part I: The Family

THE STREET

In 1911, streets were busy, social places.

'In the days before the First World War street doors in every house were always open and not shut till bedtime.'

JOHN BLAKE, *Memories of Old Poplar*

In warm weather the women sat on their front steps shelling peas, or plaiting their daughters' hair while chatting to their neighbours. Hawkers sold firewood and old clothes and musicians travelled from street to street.

'Most days in summer and winter we would see the man who played the barrel organ. This was a musical instrument with two wheels and two handles. The man would push it wherever he wanted to play. When he turned the handles it played the popular songs of the day.'

GRACE FOAKES, *Between High Walls*

Playing in the street was easier then because there was only horse-drawn traffic.

'As the seasons changed, so did our games. Marbles, conkers, and leapfrog. As you were going to school you'd see eight to ten boys leap-frogging, one over the other until they reached the school.'

TAFFY LEWIS, *Any Road*

1 Look at the photograph carefully. Imagine that you are one of the people standing in the street. Working in pairs, one of you should describe what you can see around you — the details of the houses, people and the street that catch your eye. Do you know any of the other people? What are they like? Your partner can ask you questions.

Now it is the other person's turn. Imagine you can see inside one of the houses in the terrace. What is it like? Are there any people inside the house? What are the furnishings like?

2 Work in small groups. Imagine that you are a family living in the street. Decide on roles for everyone in the group. Choose your names and ages, and any work you may do.

Prepare a tableau (a frozen picture) which will show what your family is doing at an important moment of the day — perhaps early in the morning or after work is over for the day.

3 Still in your groups, prepare a short scene which will show one of the greatest difficulties your family faces. It may be to do with work, health, living conditions or school.

You could open the play with a lively sequence of 'film-clip' scenes that introduce different families and express the variety and spirit of life in the street. (Allow no more than 15 seconds for each clip.)

To draw out the contrast between rich and poor, insert still tableaux with spoken captions depicting the characters and attitudes of the Upper Classes.

MAKING ENDS MEET

In 1911 a family that earned less than two pounds a week lived in poverty. There was no dole money. From an early age children had to do what they could to increase the weekly income. Those families that lost the battle to make ends meet had to suffer the indignity of becoming 'paupers'.

'When I was twelve my father fell out of work. There weren't no work and my mother was ill. We had no money. If you wanted help you had to go in front of the doctor on the Board of Guardians.* Then he'd come down and see what furniture you 'ad, an' if you 'ad a good home, you had to sell it. We was having dinner one day, he came, my mother had been to him for help, an' he said, 'You can make that do for twice, what's on that plate.'

JESSIE NIBLETT, *b*. 1896, Bristol

* *The Board of Guardians*: a group of church representatives whose purpose was to help the very poor.

In Jessie Niblett's case the Board of Guardians decided Jessie's parents should go to live in the workhouse, while Jessie was taken into care by her aunt. She was allowed to visit her parents once a week.

'I had to go to the lodge gate and say who I wanted, and then the man used to stamp the card I had and I had to go through . . . my mother and father used to wait for me. My mother used to come in and I remember she had a little white thing on 'er head, little white apron, and all in black. My father, he was six foot and my mother was smaller than me. I can remember the first time I seen them, they didn't bother about me, they both caught 'old of one another, they hadn't seen one another for two weeks. 'Cos they used to part them when they went in.'

1   Form into the family groups that you were in before. One member of each family group should now become a visitor for

the Board of Guardians. The family has applied to the Board of Guardians for help and the visitor arrives to make enquiries. Act out the scene.

2 Those of you who were the members of the family should now change your roles. Imagine you are now members of the Board of Guardians and are holding a meeting to decide which families should be helped. Those of you who were the visitors, present your report on the conditions you found in the house you visited. What decision does the Board come to?

3 The Board has made its decision. Working in pairs, one of you should communicate the Board's decision to the other, who is a member of one of the families. If the decision is favourable, what will this mean to the family? If the request for help has been rejected, what can the family do now?

The Portingale Family

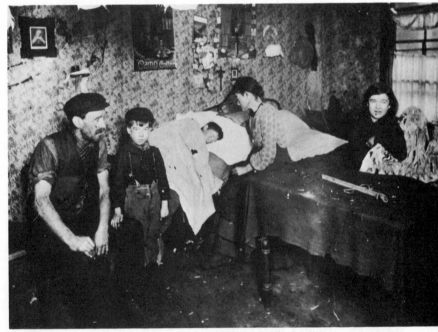

Mr Portingale	Charlie	Thomas	Mrs Portingale	Florence
35 years old	9 years old	(ill with bronchitis) 11 years old	32 years old	14 years old

This is their weekly income:

	£	s	d
Mr Portingale — railway worker	1	5	0
Mrs Portingale — takes in washing		3	0
Florence — loom operator		5	6
Thomas — dairyman's assistant (6.00–8.00 a.m.)		1	6
TOTAL	1	15	0

Every week Mrs Portingale pays these bills:

	s	d
Rent	5	9
Gas		8
Burial income	1	0
	7	5

1 Using the price list below (continued on page 60), work out how Mrs Portingale might spend the rest of her weekly income. As best you can, estimate how much food the family has to eat each day.

Mrs Portingale has £1/7s/7d to spend a week.

	Cost of item	Amount bought each week	Amount spent each week	
			s	d
Bread	3d–loaf			
Tea	1s 6d–lb			
Milk	2d–pint			
Meat	9d–1lb			
Sugar	2d–1lb			
Cheese	11d–1lb			
Butter	1s 1½d–1lb			
Potatoes	2½d–3lb			
Fish	4d–1lb			
Margarine	6d–1lb			

	Cost of item	Amount bought each week	Amount spent each week s d
Vegetables	2d–1lb		
Eggs	5d–4		
Jam	4d–1lb		
Beer	2½d–1 pint		
Cigarettes	8d–40		
Matches	1d–1 box		
Clothes	6d (Weekly contribution to clothing club)		
Coal	1s 6d–1 cwt bag		
Candles	½d–2		
Soap	3½d–1 bar		
		TOTAL	

12 pence (d) = 1 shilling.   20 shillings (s) = 1 pound.

2   Thomas has been ill for three weeks. Mrs Portingale has had to pay two doctor's bills as well as buy necessary medicines (there was no National Health Service in 1911). Without Thomas' earnings the family is sinking rapidly into debt.

Work in pairs. Mrs Portingale is in the corner shop. She has no money to buy food for her family and already owes the shopkeeper 4 s. How does she try to persuade the shopkeeper to give her more food on credit?

3   Mrs Portingale has taken in more washing to earn extra money. In desperation, she has pawned some of the washing to pay for the day's food. She intends to redeem the articles the following day when Mr Portingale receives his wages. Today, at least the family can eat.

In groups of five or six, create the scene at tea-time. The family is about to begin the meal when a knock on the door is heard. The owner of the washing has arrived a day earlier than expected . . .

4   Now compare the Atkins family with the Portingales. Mr Atkins is in prison for causing industrial unrest. Assume that Mrs Atkins gets 15s a week strike pay from the union and that Tommy earns an extra 2s/6d as a grocer's errand boy, making a total of 17s/6d.

How do Mrs Atkins and Tommy manage their weekly budget? What can they do to avoid getting deep into debt?

A modern audience might not fully appreciate the difficulties of making ends meet on wages below poverty level.

Tommy could help bridge the gap by stepping out of the scene and addressing the audience directly on the various survival methods used by the families in the street.

Extracts from stories are useful in this type of direct presentation. The Charlie Portingale story could be inserted as it stands, spoken in character to the audience.

THE RIGHT TO STRIKE

Mr Atkins' wage has been reduced from 25s to 23s. Employers in 1911 were free to do this without warning to the workforce.

What would the loss of 2s a week mean to the Portingale family? Do you think that this would be sufficient cause for strike action?

You could fade to a flashback of a workers' meeting where Mr Atkins and fellow union committee members are persuading the men of the need to take strike action for better wages and conditions.

You could project slides of striking workers onto the screen.

Before the play begins you could place campaign slogans around the walls of the hall.

You could devise a leaflet explaining the arguments in support of strike action. You could give this to the audience as they enter. Alternatively, you could print the leaflet in the play programme.

THE THREE GREATEST FEARS OF THE WORKING MAN

SICKNESS

DEBT

LOSING HIS JOB

But wages have increased by only 1%

TO THE WORKHOUSE ← SICKNESS & DEBT ← NO JOB

SO 25s a week is 25s a week and a JOB is a JOB

QUESTION: How can the working man ① protect himself against unfair dismissal and ② improve his wages and conditions.
ANSWER: By joining a UNION

THE WORKING MAN FINDS STRENGTH IN NUMBERS

Strikers marching over Willesden Railway Bridge August, 1911.

London:
140,000 railway workers
70,000 dock workers
Liverpool:
35,000 dock workers
Glasgow: 2,500 tramway workers
Rhondda Valley: 12,000 miners

63

THE FANSHAWES

Royal Ascot 1907

At the grouse shoot 1908

1   The Fanshawe family has an appointment at a photographer's studio. They wish to have some 'portraits' taken for display in the drawing room.

What sort of qualities of character do they want the photographs to express? How should they pose for the photographer to capture these qualities?

2   Tommy delivers groceries to the Fanshawe house. One day when he arrives he finds no servants around, so he takes the chance to sneak in and look at the house.

Close your eyes. Imagine you are Tommy walking through the Fanshawe house. You have never before been beyond the back door of the kitchen. What do you see? How large are the rooms? What are they used for? How are they decorated? What objects do they contain?

3   Divide into groups of six — Tommy, the Fanshawe family and the butler (or maid).

On hearing footsteps along the corridor Tommy has slipped into the dining room and hidden behind a curtain by a window. Mr and Mrs Fanshawe, Cyril and Cynthia now enter for afternoon tea. Through a gap in the curtain Tommy can see and hear everything. What sort of food is on the table? How does the behaviour of the Fanshawes differ from that of Tommy's own family?

4   In his effort to keep his head and shoulders hidden, Tommy has forgotten all about his feet . . .   What happens when he is discovered?

5   Mr Fanshawe is a magistrate dedicated to preserving 'law and order'. On 16th September 1911, this report of a case in the Juvenile Court appeared in *The Star*, London (see page 66).

In groups refer to the newspaper article. Discuss James Ritchie's attitude to the strikers. Why does he believe that the leaders of such weak-minded individuals should be made to suffer?

Do you see similarities between Mr Fanshawe and Sir James Ritchie?

6   Now assume Mr Fanshawe and Sir James Ritchie are one and the same. The leader of the printer's union is in court charged with stirring up political discontent. There are other magistrates on the bench alongside Mr Fanshawe as well as defence lawyers from the printer's union. Act out the court proceedings.

ALDERMAN RITCHIE ON STRIKES

At the City Juvenile Court today, William Stewart, aged 8, was charged with begging.

Mr Webster, of the Industrial Schools Committee, said the boy's father was a printer who had been earning £3 a week. A few months ago, however, he came out on strike and was now receiving 15s a week strike pay.

Five children — including a boy of 15 and a girl of 14—slept on one bed, and there were no bedclothes.

The home was in a shocking condition, and the parents had been convicted for neglecting their children.

Alderman Sir James Ritchie, the magistrate, expressed his indignation at a man earning £3 a week, and having a family to support, coming out on strike.

The father: 'I belong to the union, and have to do as I am told.'

Sir James: 'Yes, and you neglect your family. The boy will be sent to the Remand Home.'

In a second case of begging, where poverty as the result of the printers' strike was said to have reduced a comfortable home to 'a picture of misery', there being now practically nothing left but the beds, Mr Webster said:

'The father didn't want to come out, but was compelled to.'

Sir James said he considered it absolute nonsense for a man with the responsibilities of a family, earning good money, and for no earthly reason, to throw up his employment. The leaders of such weak-minded individuals ought to be made to suffer.

You could play this scene as a combination of two scenes:

a the Fanshawe family at tea

b Mr Fanshawe in court hearing the case of a strike leader charged with causing social unrest.

Mr Fanshawe's place at the head of the table, if raised a little, could also be his seat 'on the bench'. The accused could then stand at the other end of the table while the Fanshawe family take tea in between.

Try to exploit the possibilities for comic interplay between the two levels of the scene.

PART II: SCHOOL

GAS STREET RAGGED

Gas Street School would have looked something like the building in the photograph below.

'The classrooms are insufficient (four for 450 pupils) and one is without desks.'
'Inadequate lighting and ventilation.'
'A cloakroom with bowls and taps would be a boon.'
'The staff here must be strengthened at once.'

*from reports by His Majesty's Inspectors
on a Ragged School in Salford c. 1911*

What special difficulties do you think the teachers and the pupils have to cope with in this classroom?

In 1911, children could stay on at school until they were 14, though many left much earlier and many did not attend full-time.

The School Day

Inspection
The teacher checked finger-nails, palms and neck.

'I used to 'ave to get up every mornin' to go to this slag heap 'cos we couldn't afford to buy coal, an' on this slag heap you could 'ave it for nothin'. I've been many a time with no shoes or socks on, an' going to there you 'ad to go through a mucky yard, an' if it'd been raining, the water'd hang in there, but my feet was 'ardened to it — my feet was as hard as nails.

I still 'ad to go to school after. It was like a quick lick and a promise. 'Where's the towel, mother?' an' no grub, then

68

run to school. No breakfast, never 'eard of that in my day. When you got to school you knew what you was going to get . . . '

BILL BEES, *b.* 1909, Hanham, Gloucestershire

Assembly

'We'd start the day with a religious ceremony. Sing the hymn of the day . . . It was part of the medicine you had to take going to school.'

CHARLIE MILLER, *b.* 1906, Bristol

Reading, Writing, Arithmetic

'It was the same thing, day after day. The main education was twice one is two, an' twice two is four, an' so on. I was that browned off in school . . . I didn't care if I learnt anything or not. I would look at the clock an' think to myself, you know, I'll be glad when it's dinner time . . . '

JANE TAVENER, *b.* 1912, Exeter

History

'The history as we were taught it at school, was just what was sorted out for us as members of the British Empire. It was all dates and names and battles, the Spanish Armada, Nelson, Marlborough and all that.'

JIM HOWES, *b*. 1905, Bristol

'They used to encourage us to be proud of the flag, salute the flag when we was at school. Yes, I was proud of being British. We was always taught to be proud of the Queen and King. We was the people of the world wasn't we?'

BILL WOODS, *b*. 1902, Bristol

'I loved poetry, and the school was assembled and they stood me on top of the headmistress's desk and I had a Union Jack draped round me. And I had to recite 'Oh, where are you going to, all you big steamers? To fetch England's own grain up and down the great sea. I'm going to fetch you your bread and butter.' And somehow or other it stirred a bit of rebellion in me. I thought, "Where's my bread, where's my butter?" '

EDNA RICH, *b*. 1910, Bristol

The Problems of Being Poor at School

1 Long ago you were a pupil at Gas Street School. In your imagination return to the classroom you remember best and sit at your old desk. What do you see and hear? Walk around the room and remind yourself of the people who used to be there and the things you did. Can you remember what it *felt* like to be at school?

2 Now divide into pairs. A, a pupil from 1911, gives B, a pupil from 1986, a guided tour of the classroom. Make special note of the differences between school life in 1911 and school life today. Have any aspects remained unchanged?

3 Divide into groups of four. Make a list of all the formal activities and daily routines of Gas Street School. Create an action sequence by contrasting school routines.

4 Using the full space of the hall or drama studio, create the environment of Gas Street School. Invite groups from elsewhere in your school to come in as observers.

The layout could be based on separate classrooms or on one large classroom. To get round the problem of insufficient numbers, a group of five or six may have to represent a class of fifty pupils.

EITHER set up the lessons, activities and routines that might be happening at say, 11.00 on a Monday morning.

OR, construct a 'Day in the Life of Gas Street School' from fragments of the most typical events occurring between 9.00 a.m. and 4.00 p.m.

Introduce Gas Street Ragged School directly to the audience. This could be done by one of the pupils with the help of a large drawing of the exterior of the school. As this pupil points to each window, other pupils act out a short 'clip' of the lesson going on in that particular room. Alternatively, short tableaux of various lessons could be presented on stage.

71

TEACHERS

'Miss Dugdale, after we 'ad prayers in the big hall, she'd go round an' look at yer shoes, then she'd say, 'About turn,' we'd about turn an' she'd look at the backs of yer shoes. If you 'ad dirty shoes, 'No play. Stay in.' Well, very often our parents never 'ad enough money to buy boot polish so we used to spit on a brush to put on our shoes. Then she'd say, 'Hands out.' You'd 'ave to put yer hands out an' yer nails 'ad to be clean an' yer hands to be clean. She was a perfect governess, that one. If you only walked in front of 'er desk, you 'ad to say, 'Please excuse me, Miss Dugdale.' She'd nod and you were allowed to pass 'er desk.'

DAISY WINTLE, *b.* 1897, Bristol

from the wall of the boys' lavatory

Arm muscle for caning

12"

Cane hidden in trouser leg

Cast iron vocal cords for shouting

Old Whippem is a good man
He goes to church on Sunday
He prays to God to give him strength
To beat the boys on Monday.

'He didn't mince no matters about it. He gave it to you hot 'n holy, right over his shoulders, you know, an' right across that thumb — an' it don't half hurt across there mind. We used to put all sorts on us hands. We used to put our hands in our hair an' put a hair on it so the cane would break. It never did though.'

REG SUMMERHAYES, *b.* 1905, Bath

'There was only one teacher that I really liked, and I really loved that man. He was one of nature's gentlemen. He made teaching interesting and made you look up to him.'

VICTORIA AMEY, *b.* 1896, Bristol

Put yourself in the position of a teacher at Gas Street School in 1911. You probably feel very fortunate to have a job at all as you know of many trained teachers who are unemployed.

You must be prepared to teach all subjects — including music and drill (PE). Once a year you will be visited by the school inspectors when your class will be examined in what they have learned. If your pupils have not reached the proper standard you may not receive your annual increase in salary.

Above all, you must keep order in your classroom at all times and never allow the pupils to question your authority. (Remember the headmaster can see you through the class

Number	Date	Name of Child	Age	Offence	Nature and Amount of Punishment	By Whom Inflicted	Remarks
311	8.11	COOPER HUGH	8	Persistent idleness and inattention	2 on each hand 2 on seat	AWM	Very troublesome boy
312	19.11	WELCH PERCY	8	Arriving at school at 2.70, having been sent at 1.35	2 on each hand	AWM	
313	19.11	LONDON DONALD	8½	"	"	AWM	
314	20.11	GUEST IVOR	13	cheating in test	2 on each hand	AWM	Exam papers cancelled for same
315	21.11	NICHOLLS DENNIS	11	causing disturbance in lesson	"	AWM	Punished every day since 10.11

from the punishment book of St Barnabas' School, Bristol

partition.) How are you going to do this with a class of over 50 pupils? To help you keep order you have the cane and the punishment book. Your pupils are aware that if their names appear too often in the punishment book, they will not get a good reference, and they need a good reference to stand any chance of getting a job.

1 In groups of three or four work out what you would consider to be the four most important rules for classroom discipline that should be observed at all times in Gas Street School.

Write them on paper and then display them on the wall.

Compare your set of rules with those of other groups. Which rules appear most frequently?

2 Set out tables and chairs in a formal classroom arrangement. If possible, raise the teacher's desk. Choose one person to be teacher. (Your own teacher, could, of course, be teacher.)

It is an English lesson and today there will be a spelling test of words that should have been learnt since yesterday. For various reasons, however, not all the pupils have done the work.

Experiment with various teaching approaches to this situation. How might a strict teacher use it to reaffirm his/her authority in the classroom? Could the teacher handle the lesson sympathetically without losing control of classroom discipline?

Work out which methods are the most practical and successful. Keep in mind the special circumstances of Gas Street School — the layout of classrooms, the numbers of pupils etc. Before acting out the lesson you should establish the rules that would be understood (though perhaps not fully accepted) by the pupils.

Remember that in 1911 it was probably just as difficult to resist playing up teacher as it is today.

Bill Harding's Story

'Why I've got my bad ear is because I went to sleep sat at the desk, where I was half-starved. Didn't get enough food when we was children. I went to sleep in the class. The teacher called me out. He said, "Harding!" Made me jump when he shouted. Had a terrible loud voice. I went out an' he give I the piece of chalk an' I had to put where the apostrophe 's' should be. An' I put 'n in the wrong place. I put it at the beginning of the word instead of at the end of the word. And he caught me, crash! And before I fell to the ground, he hit me on the other side, hooked me up again. He said, "You weren't paying attention, were you?"'

BILL HARDING, *b*. 1901, Bristol

1 Imagine that this incident has just taken place in Gas Street School and that you are a pupil in Bill's class. You have seen what has happened and you are very angry about it. Dare you say anything directly to the teacher? If so, what would be the best way to do it?

2 On your way home from school you see another teacher marking books alone in a classroom. You know this teacher disapproves of using the cane. Here is a good opportunity to express your concern to him/her about Bill Harding.

3 Now divide into groups of four. The sympathetic teacher has decided to visit the Harding home to speak with Bill's parents to find out more about the family's circumstances.

Bill is there with his ear poorly bandaged. He has not seen a doctor. Are Bill's parents angry about the incident? How do they react to the presence of the teacher?

4 The following day.

What should the sympathetic teacher do now? Speak with Bill's teacher? Raise the issue with the headmaster? The sympathetic teacher's dilemma is heightened by the fact that some days previously he/she caught Bill going through the pockets of some coats. Bill has been caught stealing on several previous occasions too.

5 A few days later.

It is 'JUDGEMENT DAY' — the day when His Majesty's Inspectors pay their annual visit to Gas Street School.

'And the great ones duly arrived, putting the fear of God into everyone on the staff. But *we* loved them! Like Dutch uncles they went round the classes, treating us with a sort of old-world courtesy, always enquiring, and making us feel that, in school at least, girls and boys were the people who mattered.'

ROBERT ROBERTS, *A Ragged Schooling*

For the following sequence enlist the help of two teachers to play the Inspectors.

NOTES FOR THE INSPECTORS

In your last report on Gas Street School you were critical of the large number of entries in the punishment book. You pointed out that 'there is too much discipline at the expense of learning'.

On this visit you are keen to find out if standards have improved in both discipline and learning.

Begin with the arrival of the Inspectors into Bill Harding's class. The class teacher is present as well as the headmaster (your teacher playing the role?) and representatives from the school governors.

Bill Harding is also present with his ear still bandaged.

The Inspectors have some questions about the work the class has been engaged in recently.

6 The Inspectors wish to enquire further into the case of Bill Harding.

They may call for interview: a Bill Harding   b His parents
c The teacher who hit him   d The head and governors
e The sympathetic teacher

(This sort of enquiry would normally be conducted in private, but here the class could be present as non-participatory observers.)

7 Divide into groups of four.

Before making a statement about the Bill Harding case the Inspectors want to talk with the pupils without any teachers present. They want to know about school matters other than discipline that are of special concern to the pupils.

Each group should work out its own priorities and present them to the Inspectors.

8 After retiring briefly, the Inspectors call the headmaster and governors to a meeting to tell them the main points they intend to include in their report. How will the headmaster and governors respond to the Inspectors' conclusions?

9 What might the headmaster and governors have to say to each other after the Inspectors have departed?

Would the headmaster want to speak with his staff? If so, what might he say?

The next inspection is only twelve months away. What sort of changes, if any, do they intend to make before then?

At this point the scene could move to another part of Gas Street School. This would introduce into the play a different class and teacher, and another aspect of life in the school.

It is possible that many exciting school scenes involving new situations and characters will arise out of improvisation. If so, think carefully about how they might be used as a basis for the Gas Street School story in the play.

To fit a new story line into the play you will need to do some fundamental restructuring of the plot especially in the first half. If this task seems too daunting you could insert extra school scenes after scenes three and four without causing too much disturbance to the play's existing structure.

THE MUMPS ACADEMY

'Leave must be asked from the class teacher before speaking to another pupil. Leave must be obtained from both class teachers before speaking to a pupil in another class. Conversations must be finished in the place where permission is given and may not be carried on in dressing rooms, corridors or staircases.'

Ladies' School Hillary Mount
WOODHOUSE LANE, LEEDS,
Conducted by The Misses Giles, and Visiting Masters

The Course of Instruction includes Reading, Writing, Arithmetic, English Literature, and Composition, Needlework, &c., &c., Accomplishments, French, German, Music, Singing, Painting, Drawing, Dancing, Calisthenics, Wax Flower Making, &c. Private lessons given in the Accomplishments.

The House is very large, pleasantly and healthily situated, one School-room being thirty feet long, and very lofty. Spacious dormitories and bath. The number of resident Pupils being limited, every comfort is afforded. The domestic arrangements are under the superintendence of Mrs Giles, and are those of a private family.

Terms for Day and Resident Pupils on application
A Class for Little Boys.

REFERENCES
KINDLY PERMITTED TO PARENTS OF PUPILS, MINISTERS
AND GENTLEMEN.

'Leave must be asked from the class teacher before speaking to another pupil. Leave must be obtained from both class teachers before speaking to a pupil in another class. Conversations must be finished in the place where permission is given and may not be carried on in dressing rooms, corridors or staircases.'

Advertisement for a Girls' Independent School

'The accomplished young lady is poised, charming, sociable, graceful. She is conscious, at all times, of her duty to promote the happiness of others.'

78

Cynthia and Lily could at this point step into a dreamworld music-hall. A spotlight, swelling music and audience reactions will help to create the atmosphere. With 'Come on girls. We're off to Blackpool . . . ' the dreamworld dissolves back to reality.

Another good opportunity to insert a dreamworld scene — the lovely Cynthia weaves a spell of the seaside over Tommy and transports him (and the other Scruff Kids) on a dream trip to Blackpool. Use sound effects — brass band, waves and seagulls, fairground organ — and build in different types of movement.

Begin this scene with a group of Gas Street strikers peeping through a window of the Mumps Academy. What do they see? How does it differ from Gas Street School? Alternatively, the scene could begin from inside the Mumps Academy where a lesson is in progress.

THE SCHOOL STRIKES

In 1889, the first great wave of school strikes swept the country causing alarm among Education Authorities everywhere.

comments from Educational News, *5 October 1889*

Were the strikes a carefully planned conspiracy to destroy the social order?

> 'How did the schoolboys receive the signal for united action? Such movements do not spring up spontaneously. They are evidence of a deep conspiracy against social order. The Doom of the Empire must be near at hand if the country is honeycombed with secret societies of children.'

Dundee Advertiser, 11 October 1889

In 1911 strikes broke out again.

1   Divide into groups of six or eight. An emergency meeting of the Education Committee has been convened to discuss the latest outbreak and to draw up measures that might be taken to prevent them spreading to the schools in its area.

2   How would members of the Committee answer questions from a reporter who, sensing that there might be a good story in the strikes, is anxious to know details of the Committee's plan of action?

Tommy Atkins — Strike Leader

'Sam Brick he was the ringleader ... He was a quiet chap, must have had trade unionism in his blood, got it from his father, I suppose. Well, it was a Friday. We was talking in the playground, "We ought to go out on strike ..."'

CHARLIE DALLIMORE, *b.* 1900, Bristol

'My father was an ILP [Independent Labour Party] man and he had a large collection of books, Robert Blatchford, Bernard Shaw, H. G. Wells. It was like a university. Well, I was only twelve years old and I read *The Rights of Man*, Tom Paine.'

JIM FLOWERS, *b.* 1900, Bristol

Like Sam Brick and Jim Flowers, Tommy Atkins would have learned the ABC of trade unionism from his father.

1   Imagine that Tommy has formed a pupils' union to fight for better conditions at Gas Street School. Following a meeting in the playground the caretaker finds this note on a crumpled piece of paper:

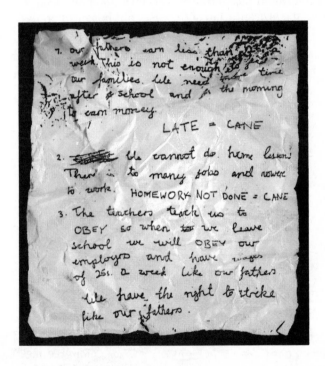

Two days later Tommy and his mother receive a letter asking them to attend a meeting with members of the Education Committee to discuss 'the very grave matter of the note found in Gas Street School.'

What would Mrs Atkins have to say to Tommy after she has read the letter? Act out this scene.

2   In groups, act out the meeting with the Education Committee. Does Tommy crack under the pressure or does he see this as a chance to explain his union's proposals for Gas Street School?

Other pupils including Sammy Simkins and his mother are called in after Tommy.

3   Following this meeting, Tommy and the pupils' union committee prepare a letter to the local press as a statement of their claims and their arguments in support of them. Working in groups, draft this letter.

> You could alter this scene to include more of the reasons behind the call for strike action. This could be based around a presentation of the case that has been prepared by Tommy and the pupils' union committee.

Fall in and Follow Me

Pickets, some of whom had pinned on their coats pieces of cardboard on which the word 'Picket' was written, went to various schools and induced the lads to come out. In the afternoon, gangs of boys paraded the streets visiting the schools. At several of the schools policemen were stationed, as there had been some stone-throwing and the pickets had attacked schoolboys whom they had caught in the playgrounds. Policemen in plain clothes were also on duty. Whenever a schoolmaster made his appearance he was hooted by the strikers. Some of the headmasters interviewed yesterday, said such flagrant conduct would not be allowed to pass unnoticed, and they had a rod in pickle for the boys.

Birmingham Daily Mail,
13th September, 1911

At Maryport yesterday a strong picket from the Grasslot Council School marched up to the Council School, Maryport, to bring the boys 'out' there. The headmaster sent the upper standard boys out to 'capture' the ringleaders. The picket retired to the Market Place, but there made a stand, and a battle royal ensued. The leader of the Grasslot boys was secured, but fought so hard with feet and fists that he escaped again.

Greenock Telegraph,
16th September, 1911

At Enfield about 200 boys of the Southbury Road School abandoned lesson books and picketed the school gates. Smaller children, whom they endeavoured to intimidate, ran home with the cry of 'I'll tell my muvver', and in some cases, the little ones were escorted through the school gates by mothers who threatened to 'wallop' any boys who dared to stand between their Teddies and the fountain of knowledge.

Northern Daily Telegraph,
15th September, 1911

Our representative then had an interview with Mr H. Dee, the headmaster. To our question as to whether it was true that a hundred of his boys were playing truant, or, to be in the fashion, were out 'on strike', he said there was nothing like that number. He estimated the strikers at about a score, mostly senior boys. He pointed out the senior class where there were not more than about eleven vacant places, and he thought it was possible that a few of the smaller boys from the junior classes had also gone off for a holiday.

'What is the cause of the boys going out in this way?' he was asked.

'I cannot say,' replied Mr Dee. 'I have questioned some of the boys, and they said that the "strikers" were out against homework. They certainly have no grievance against the school.'

Illustrated News,
15th September, 1911

Schoolboys on strike in Shoreditch, 1911

Insert strike 'news flashes' from reporters around the country. Other 'news flashes' could be used to link scenes eleven to fifteen. If you decide to have a 'strike operations' board, you could mark each incident on the board.

Insert a short scene in which Mr Whippem answers questions about the Gas Street School strike from a reporter for the local newspaper. Exploit the contrast between Mr Whippem's public image and his reactions in the following scene.

Project onto the screen a picture of soldiers in trenches in the First World War.

After the narrator's speech, mix into the swelling music the sound of beatings offstage. Project other battlefield pictures and perhaps end the play with the distant voice of a teacher reading the attendance register, giving the effect of a list of war dead.

Songs From The Play

Down At Our School

We March To Our Places

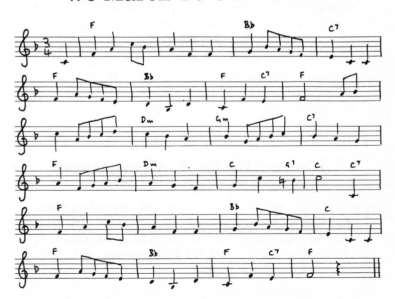

Daddy Wouldn't
Buy Me A Bow-Wow

We're Off In A Motor Car

The Corporation Muckcart

Note: There are no fixed tunes for the other songs included in the play.

BOOKS FOR FURTHER RESEARCH

Most of the quotes and references in the resource material were found in the following books. If you are interested in doing any further research you will find a lot of other valuable information about the strikes and their social setting in these books.

1   Accounts of the School Strikes:
Children's Strikes in 1911, Dave Marson (History Workshop Pamphlet, Ruskin College, Oxford, 1973)
'Hooligans or Rebels?' — an Oral History of Working Childhood and Youth 1889–1939, Stephen Humphries (Basil Blackwell, 1981)

2   Photographs of Edwardian England:
Victorian and Edwardian Children from Old Photographs, A. J. & D. K. Pierce (B. T. Batsford, 1980)
The Edwardians in Photographs, Paul Thompson & Gina Harkell (B. T. Batsford, 1979)
The Golden Years 1903–1913, Gordon Winter (David & Charles, 1975)

3   Social Conditions — at home and in school:
Life in Edwardian England, Robert Cecil (B. T. Batsford, 1969)
Edwardian England 'Then and There Series', Alan Delgado (Longman, 1967)
The Edwardians, J. B. Priestley (Heinemann, 1970)
Edwardian Children, Joanna Smith (Hutchinson, 1983)
Ordinary Lives a Hundred Years Ago, Carol Adams (Virago, 1982)
Schools 'Past and Present Series', Alan Dures (B. T. Batsford, 1971)
The Classic Slum, Robert Roberts (Pelican, 1973)
A Ragged Schooling, Robert Roberts (Fontana, 1978)
Round About A Pound A Week, Maud Pember Reeves (Virago, 1979)